LAW, MEDICINE AND ETHICS: ESSAYS IN HONOUR OF LORD JAKOBOVITS

Norman Rockwell Visits a Family Doctor: *The Saturday Evening Post* (1947).

LAW, MEDICINE AND ETHICS: ESSAYS IN HONOUR OF LORD JAKOBOVITS

Contributors

The Rt Hon the Lord Woolf of Barnes PC
Professor Sir Ian Kennedy
The Baroness Deech of Cumnor
Professor Sir Liam Donaldson CMO

Edited by

John Carrier
Gloria Freilich
Victor Hoffbrand
Santilal Parbhoo

The Cancerkin Centre
The Royal Free Hospital
London
2007

First published in 2007 by Cancerkin®, London

© 2007 Cancerkin®, London

ISBN 978-0-9554799-0-8

Typeset in 11/12pt Baskerville by Columns Design Ltd, RG4 7DH, Reading
Printed in Great Britain at Cambridge University Press

CONTENTS

ACKNOWLEDGEMENTS

Cancerkin and members of the Lecture Committee are deeply grateful to the following for generously supporting the Lord Jakobovits Commemorative Lectures (2001–04)

Jarvis Astaire Esq OBE
Mrs Rita Eker
Mrs Marta Gross
The late Philip Mishon OBE
Sir Harry Solomon
Mr & Mrs Nicholas Springer

Also for the generous sponsorship of this publication the Lecture Committee are most grateful to The Rachel Charitable Trust.

The Norman Rockwell illustration 'Norman Rockwell Visits a Family Doctor': *The Saturday Evening Post* (1947) is reproduced by kind permission of Mr John Rockwell and Mr Thomas Rockwell – The Norman Rockwell Family Agency.

We thank Mrs Golda Gold for her patience and dedication in re-typing manuscripts for this volume.

THE LORD JAKOBOVITS COMMEMORATIVE LECTURES: AN INTRODUCTION

Cancerkin was the first breast cancer charity in the UK founded 20 years ago on a hospital site, at the Royal Free Hospital, London. Its objectives include treatment, supportive care and rehabilitation, education and research.

Lord Jakobovits was an important patron of Cancerkin and a decision was taken to honour his memory with a short series of lectures, designed to address issues central to Lord Jakobovits' intellectual and ethical concerns.

This publication is based on generous contributions of time, energy and commitment from four eminent experts in the fields of law, medicine and ethics. Each agreed to speak to an invited audience of lay and professional people and to answer questions on the content of their presentations.

In reviewing the role played by the law and the courts, the Lord Chief Justice, Lord Woolf, set the context for the series by reminding us that:

> Judicial proceedings allow ethical questions to be treated in a thorough and neutral fashion. Answers can be given which, whether right or wrong, have a fair degree of finality and legitimacy.

Whether or not one agrees with Lord Woolf's view on the judicial proceedings, there is little doubt that the case law examples he used, from euthanasia, contraception, abortion, the surgery on conjoined twins, consent to treatment, and the taking of sperm from a deceased husband, (especially in the case of Mrs Blood) are suffused with ethical considerations. The law is never static; witness the case of *Chester v Afshar* [2004] UKHL (which could now be said to be the leading case, replacing the Sidaway case referred to in Lord Woolf's lecture).

Baroness Deech, an eminent Oxford lawyer and former Chair of the Human Fertilisation and Embryology Authority (HFEA), surveys the role of legislation as being instrumental in providing 'a framework that translates ethical considerations into practical applications' through the agency of the HFEA. She concentrates on the decision of the Authority to refuse Mrs Blood's request to use her deceased husband's sperm, in line with the Statute and the absence of consent. It is particularly instructive for the reader to examine Lord Woolf's reasons for allowing Mrs Blood to take the sperm abroad for implantation. Lord Jakobovits would, I believe, have found Lady

Deech's adherence to the intention of the Statute admirable but would probably have supported Lord Woolf's humane and flexible interpretation of the Statute. Nevertheless, both decisions have in common what Lady Deech describes as the 'greatest ethical issues imaginable'.

Professor Sir Ian Kennedy, a highly respected academic lawyer, provides an insight into the purposes, mechanics and principles underpinning the Bristol Inquiry. These insights are truly groundbreaking and original. Rarely has a Chairman of a major public inquiry, of national interest with the highest of political profiles, explained with such clarity his thinking on what such an inquiry should achieve. In his presentation the ethics of 'discovering the truth' is matched by the ethics of 'facilitating understanding'.

To place 'catharsis', healing' and 'understanding' on the same level as 'accountability' for 'what went wrong' demonstrates abundantly the ethics of concern for all involved; parents, professionals and the wider public. Rigour and humanity shine through this contribution, which might well become a role model for conducting a public inquiry. At all times the question, 'How will this inquiry serve the interests of the bereaved parents?', dominates the discussion. It is noteworthy that since these lectures were given, Sir Ian Kennedy has become Chair of the Health Care Commission, the body charged with assessing the quality of health care delivered by the NHS.

Sir Ian's concerns fit perfectly with the Chief Medical Officer Sir Liam Donaldson's statement:

> It is not necessary to be a specialist steeped in the concepts and schools of ethical thought to appreciate ethical dimensions of daily medical practice. The fundamental ethical principle in the delivery of health care is the respect for the individual patient.

Sir Liam demonstrates the importance of respect for the patient by referring to health service and systems reforms, the duty of quality, clinical governance, revalidation of doctors by the GMC, Patient and Public Involvement Forums, the creation of Patient Advisory Liaison Schemes and the National Patient Safety Agency. Although to the lay person this list may seem overly bureaucratic, the existence of such arrangements surely supports Sir Liam's view that 'good quality care is now judged in explicit ways'.

So, we are indeed fortunate to have in print the observations of this distinguished group. It is certain that Lord Jakobovits would have approved of such a critical mass of intellectual and practical expertise being devoted to ensuring that the link between ethics, law and medicine is kept centre stage.

At the time of publication it is interesting to note how important the themes common to all our speakers (the necessity of the medical profession to be sensitive to the needs of patients and of their carers) came to a head in Lord Joffe's Assisted Dying for the Terminally Ill Bill which was debated in the House of Lords on 12th May 2006. The debate was a dramatic demonstration of the relationship between law, ethics and medicine. On this occasion, the Bill was defeated but the argument continues.

Cancerkin is grateful to each contributor to the Lord Jakobovits series and is delighted that these lectures will reach a wider audience.

John Carrier PhD, *Lecture Chairman*

BIOGRAPHIES

THE LORD JAKOBOVITS

Born in 1921 in Königsberg, Germany, Immanuel Jakobovits grew up in a home immersed in religion and medicine. At the age of 16, he was the first of his family to escape the growing Nazi terror of his homeland, settling in London. His studies at Jews' College led to a BA with honours and a Minister's Diploma, and at the age of 20, he was appointed to his first pulpit. By 1947, with a rabbinical degree from Etz Chaim Yeshiva, he had moved to the Great Synagogue in Duke's Place, London.

In Paris, in 1949, he married Amélie Munk and that same year, was appointed Chief Rabbi of Ireland, where he served until 1958. During that period, in 1955, he attained a PhD in Jewish Medical Ethics, from London University.

The family then moved to New York where, as Founder Rabbi of Fifth Avenue Synagogue, he served until 1967.

As Chief Rabbi of the United Hebrew Congregations of Great Britain and the Commonwealth, for almost a quarter of a century until 1991, Immanuel Jakobovits made outstanding contributions to spiritual, intellectual and political life. A brilliant thinker and never one to avoid controversy, his influence often penetrated far beyond the community of his faith, introducing Jewish ethics into areas typically regarded as secular, such as medicine and biotechnology.

Recognition of his service, influence and lifetime achievements came first through the award of a knighthood in 1981. In 1988, Immanuel Jakobovits was elevated to the peerage as Lord Jakobovits of Regent's Park, thus becoming the first rabbi to sit in the House of Lords.

In 1990, he was awarded the distinguished Templeton Prize for Religion.

Outstanding among his contributions to Jewish scholarship is his 'Jewish Medical Ethics', which is acknowledged as the classical work on the subject. His other books include *Jewish Law Faces Modern Problems*, *The Timely and the Timeless*. *The Authorized Daily Prayer Book*, *If Only My People* and *Dear Chief*

Rabbi, as well as numerous pamphlets and articles. Lord Jakobovits contributed most of the Jewish Medical ethics entries to the *Encyclopaedia Judaica*.

Questions in medical ethics raised by Lord Jakobovits go far beyond Judaism, and have a universal resonance and significance for those of other faiths and those of none. This series of lectures commemorates Lord Jakobovits' life and his main contribution: the ethical dimension in medical care.

THE RT HON THE LORD WOOLF OF BARNES PC

Lord Woolf was born in Newcastle and educated at Glasgow Academy and Fettes College, Edinburgh, finally graduating from University College, London. He was called to the bar, The Inner Temple, in 1954.

After National Service in the 15th/19th King's Royal Hussars, with secondment to army legal services, Lord Woolf began practicing as a barrister in 1956. From 1972–79, he served as a Recorder of the Crown Court, and was then appointed a High Court Judge in the Queen's Bench Division. During the ensuing 10 years, Lord Woolf served successfully as Lord Justice of Appeal and Lord of Appeal in Ordinary. In 1996 he was appointed Master of the Rolls and in 2000, Lord Chief Justice of England and Wales.

He continues to find time to chair or preside over a prodigious number of committees and societies, in the furtherance of education, administration of law and social welfare. Examples among his many interests and commitments are the Board of Management of the Institute of Advanced Legal Studies, the Lord Chancellor's Advisory Committee on Legal Education, the Civil Justice Council, the Central Council of Jewish Social Services, the Public Records Society, Association of Members of Boards of Visitors.

Lord Woolf holds honorary doctorates from the Universities of Buckingham, Bristol, London, Anglia PolyUniversity and Manchester Metropolitan. He is also an Honorary Member of the British Academy and in 1994 was Pro-Chancellor of London University.

In 1990, Lord Woolf carried out the inquiry into prison disturbances following the Strangeways riots, completing part 11 with Judge Tumin. The report was published in 1991. He also conducted the inquiry into Access to Justice between 1994 and 1996. The reform of the Civil Justice Procedures in England and Wales, known as 'The Woolf Reforms' are a direct consequence of this inquiry, both simplifying the legal system and making it more understandable to the lay public.

His publications include *Protecting the Public: the new challenge* (Hamlyn Lecture); *Declaratory Judgement*, 2nd Edition, edited with J. Woolf; and Joint Editor de Smith, *Judicial Review of Administrative Action*, 5th Edition.

Lord Woolf has been married for 44 years and he and his wife, Margaret, have three sons.

PROFESSOR SIR IAN KENNEDY LLD

Professor Sir Ian Kennedy chaired the Public Inquiry held between 1998 and 2001 into the management of children requiring complex heart surgery at Bristol Royal Infirmary and this was the focus of his lecture. Sir Ian has had a long experience of serving public enquiries in which complex questions of medical ethics have been at the centre.

Ian McColl Kennedy, born in 1941, graduated from University College London and the University of California, Berkeley. He was a Ford Foundation Fellow at Yale University and the University of Mexico and a visiting Professor at University of California, Los Angeles and University of San Diego. He has held the Chairs of Law and Medical Ethics at King's College London and of Health Law, Ethics and Policy at University College London.

Sir Ian was called to the Bar in 1974 and made an Honorary Bencher of his Inn in 1996. His public service commitments, especially those relating to medical science, have led him to serve on numerous committees and investigatory bodies, including:

- Panel of Appointed Persons at the Public Hearings on the Licensing of Depo Provera, DHSS (1982–3)

- Medicines Commission, DHSS (1984–91)

- General Medical Council (1984–93)
  Standards Committee (1984–93)
  Preliminary Proceedings Committee (1987–89)
  Working Party on Aids (1988)
  Working Party on Disciplinary Procedures (1987–89)
  Working Party on Confidentiality (1990–1)
  Working Party on Revision of Professional Guidelines
  (as co-member (1993–6)
  Consultant (1996-)

- Expert Advisory Group on Aids, Department of Health (1987–94)
  Working Party on HIV infected Health Care Workers (1991)

- Committee to Review the Report of the Advisory Group on the Use of Foetuses and Foetal Material for Research
  (Polkinghorne Committee) DHSS (1988–89)

- Chairman, Nuffield Council on Bioethics (1998-)
  (Founding Member 1991-)

- Board of Governors of St Bartholomew's Hospital Medical School (1991–5)

- Chairman, Secretary of State's Health Advisory Group on Xenotransplantation, DoH (1995–6)

- Chairman, Minister of Agriculture's Advisory Group on Quarantine and Rabies MAFF (1997–98)

- Advisory Committee on Medical Countermeasures MOD (1998-)

- External Adviser, Survey of Porton Down Volunteer Service Programme, MOD (2001-)

- Ethics Committee of the Royal College of Nursing (1984–89), Royal College of General Practitioners (1988–90) and the British Medical Association (1989–98)

- Archbishop of Canterbury's Advisory Group on Medical Ethics (1992-)

- Centre of Medical Law and Ethics, King's College London, of which he was the Founder in 1976 and President from 1992–7.

In 1994, he served on the International Forum on Transplant Ethics and in 1997, on the Governing Council of the Committee on Publication Ethics (British Medical Journal) and in the same year, on the Genetics Committee of the Association of British Insurers. From 1998–2000, Professor Kennedy was a member of the working Party on research on Human Subjects for the Royal College of Psychiatrists.

Publications include *Unmasking Medicine* (1981); *Treat me Right* (1988); *Medical Law: Text with Materials*, (3rd ed 2000); *Principles of Medical Law* (editor with A. Grubb, 1998) in addition to numerous papers, articles, radio and television programmes.

Professor Sir Ian Kennedy is currently Chairman of the Healthcare Commission.

BARONESS DEECH OF CUMNOR
DBE, MA

Born in London, Ruth Deech studied law at Oxford, followed by graduate work at Brandeis University, USA. She was called to the bar in 1967. After working for the Law Commission on divorce reform and teaching law in Canada, she took up her post as Fellow and Tutor in Law at St Anne's College, Oxford in 1970 until being elected Principal of the college in 1991. After her retirement in 2004, the college named its latest building after her – the Ruth Deech Building.

From 1994 to 2002, Ruth Deech chaired the Human Fertilisation and Embryology Authority, a body established by law to regulate IVF treatments and to give advice to the public and to governments on new developments in the field of assisted reproduction. She is an honorary Bencher of the Inner Temple, a Rhodes Trustee, a governor of University College School, a Fellow of the Royal Society of Medicine, a fellow of the Society of Advanced Legal Studies and a fellow of the European Academy of Sciences and Arts. She is Pro-Vice-Chancellor of Oxford University and Chairman of its Admissions Committee. From 2002 to 2006 she served as a Governor of the BBC.

Since 2004, she has been the first independent Adjudicator for Higher Education, tasked with receiving student complaints from all 147 universities in England and Wales.

In 2002, Ruth Deech was appointed Dame Commander of the Order of the British Empire and in 2005 she was created a life peer.

PROFESSOR SIR LIAM
DONALDSON MSc, MD, FRCS(ED),
FFPHM, FRCP, FRCP(ED), FMEDSCI

Over a 30 year career, Sir Liam Donaldson has worked in all sectors of health care: hospital medicine, general practice, public health, academic medicine, health service management and central government.

This has taken him from a surgical training in Birmingham, to teaching and research posts at the University of Leicester (where he was also admissions tutor for the Medical School), to a part-time general practice role in Uppingham Road Health Centre, Leicester, to regional public health and management posts in the north east of England and Yorkshire, latterly with responsibility as Regional Director for meeting the health and health care needs of seven million people.

In 1998 Sir Liam became the fifteenth Chief Medical Officer for England in a line of succession that dates back to 1858. The Chief Medical Officer supports the Secretary of State for Health on all matters relating to the health of the nation and on clinical aspects of the National Health Service. He is the Government's chief adviser on health issues and as such can be called upon to advise Ministers in other departments across government as well as the Prime Minister. In addition, he is responsible for representing the United Kingdom on health matters within the European community and internationally.

Since taking up post, Sir Liam's work has very much been in the public eye. He has been involved in responding to major issues of public concern such as the retention and storage of children's organs after post-mortem, the clinical audit of the practice of Dr Harold Shipman and the Kennedy Inquiry into the Bristol children's heart surgery service.

He has published several major reports aimed at producing important changes or reforms in the medical and health field. For example, *Stem Cell Research: Medical Progress with Responsibility* became the cornerstone of the Government's approach to the controversial issue of therapeutic cloning (August 2000). *The Expert Patient: A New Approach to Chronic Disease Management for the 21st Century* set the framework for an important shift of emphasis in the treatment of chronic disease, from patient passivity to informed self-management (September, 2001). *Getting Ahead of The Curve – A Strategy for Infectious Diseases* is the first co-ordinated strategic approach to infectious disease management in the history of the NHS. The report recommended a major modernization programme to create a new system to prevent, investigate and control the threat from infectious disease and to address health protection more widely. The main focus of his recommendations was the creation of a new National Infection Control and Health Protection Agency.

Sir Liam Donaldson is recognized as a leading international voice on the issue of health care quality and patient safety. Since coming into post, he has helped to establish a comprehensive framework for assuring and improving the quality of NHS care. His landmark work in developing the concept of clinical governance, his seminal report on patient safety (*An Organisation With A Memory*, published in 2000) and his recasting of the approach to dealing with poor practitioner performance (*Supporting Doctors, Protecting Patients*, published in 1999) have all helped to make quality the central feature of the NHS in the 21st Century.

Sir Liam's Report 'Good doctors, safer patients' (DoH July 2006) was published with the aim of promoting good medical practice and protecting patients.

Sir Liam has had a distinguished professional and academic career. A graduate of the Universities of Bristol, Birmingham and Leicester, he has been awarded honorary degrees by the Universities of Bristol, Portsmouth, Leicester, Huddersfield, Cranfield and East Anglia. He holds an honorary Chair in Applied Epidemiology at the University of Newcastle upon Tyne. He was awarded the College Medal by the Royal College of Surgeons of Edinburgh in June 2000. Sir Liam has published over one hundred peer-reviewed papers in medical journals, is co-author of a standard text book of public health (which has been in continuous print for 20 years) and has contributed chapters to a further 20 medical texts.

In the 2002 New Year Honours List, Sir Liam received a knighthood in recognition of his achievements in health and health care.

THE JUDICIARY, MEDICINE AND ETHICS

**Inaugural Lecture of the series, delivered on
7th February 2001 by The Rt Hon the Lord Woolf,
Lord Chief Justice of England and Wales**

ABSTRACT

The relationship between law and medical ethics interested Lord Jakobovits deeply.

Recent events involving members of the medical profession have caused the full intensity of the media searchlights to be focussed on medical practises. The aim of this paper is to show the extent to which the courts can and should support the medical profession in recognizing their increased responsibility resulting from scientific advance.

Although it will never be a substitute for proper standards of professional ethics, the law can provide a base below which standards should not fall and guidance as to what actions are lawful. If an action is unlawful, then it will almost certainly be unethical.

Thus a new declaratory or advisory role has developed for the courts in relation to medico-legal issues, departing from the traditional approach of solving legal issues after the event and instead giving advice on what the legal position would be if an anticipated event happened.

These issues include reproductive rights, especially abortion, contraceptive advice to girls under the age of consent, euthanasia, the challenges to professional behaviour posed by the 1998 Human Rights Act and the ethical and legal framework that determines critical 'life' impact decisions.

I am confident that the subject of my talk this evening is one which would have deeply interested Lord Jakobovits. It is indeed a subject we both discussed at a seminar held under the distinguished Chairmanship of Professor Sir Ian Kennedy at King's College London. I spoke from the standpoint of a judge and Lord Jakobovits of course as a rabbi. Lord Jakobovits spoke as an expert. He had written extensively upon the relationship between Jewish law and medical ethics. This had been the subject of his thesis that resulted in his being awarded a Doctorate in Philosophy by London University in 1955. It was the subject of his book *Jewish Medical Ethics*[1] originally published in 1959. This book was the first comprehensive and comparative treatise on the subject and was followed by an enlarged edition in 1975. The enlarged edition dealt with the remarkable developments which had taken place over the preceding twenty years. Lord Jakobovits is still generally regarded as the pre-eminent religious authority on this subject. If proof of this is required, it is provided by the fact that prior to the vote in the House of Lords on therapeutic cloning on 22nd January this year, the nine top religious leaders in this country wrote and reminded the members of the House of Lords:

> In an earlier debate on human cloning held in the House two years ago our late colleague Lord Jakobovits warned that 'caution is the order of the day' reminding us that 'one slight miscalculation' could lead to implications for future generations 'that cannot be undone'.

Unfortunately my subject has become much more topical than when I first selected it. Recent events involving members of the medical profession have caused the full intensity of the media searchlights to be focussed on medical practices. Earlier this month, I also happened to be giving a lecture on a medicine-related subject. It was misinterpreted by those who were not present and had not read what I said as an attack on the medical profession. It was not an attack. I was explaining why I felt that the scrutiny by the courts of medical practices in the past had been too lax and why the position today was more satisfactory. My subject today, because it includes the word 'ethics' is clearly closer to the area of public interest and so I make it clear that nothing I am about to say is in anyway intended to criticise the medical profession. To the contrary, my primary aim is to show the extent to which the law can and should support the medical profession in their hugely increased responsibilities resulting from the pace of the march forward of science.

I was certainly not and am not an authority on the subject of medical ethics. But there is no dispute that the public in recent times has become deeply disturbed by some professional practices. It is this which makes Lord Jakobovits' contribution to the subject still so significant . The whole problem has recently been frankly, openly and constructively challenged by Sir Donald Irvine, President of the General Medical Council.[2] Part of Sir Donald's answer to the problem was to call for a new professionalism.

Although the law will never be a substitute for proper standards of professional ethics, the law can be supportive. It can provide a base below which standards should not fall. It can provide guidance as to what actions are lawful and unlawful. The fact that action is lawful does not mean it is necessarily ethical but if what is proposed is unlawful, then it will certainly also be unethical. Obviously, it can not be ethical for a doctor to treat a patient in a way which is unlawful.

Until fairly recently, usually, the only way in which the courts could give guidance was by giving judgments *after* the damage was alleged to have been done. However, early in my career as a young judge, by coincidence, I played a part in developing a new role for the courts in relation to medico-legal issues. The new role was a declaratory or advisory role for the courts. This involved departing from the traditional approach of the courts of solving legal issues after the event and instead giving advice on what would be the legal position if an anticipated event happened.

The first case was brought in 1980. The case was commenced by the Royal College of Nursing of the UK against the Department of Health.[3] The Royal College were concerned that their members were being asked to perform acts in connection with termination of pregnancy, unsupervised by medical practitioners. Such acts were unlawful notwithstanding section 1(1) of the Abortion Act 1967, because that section only allowed pregnancies to be terminated by medical practitioners.. What was happening was that the medical practitioner would start the process using prostaglandin and then leave the patient in the care of the nurse. I decided, and the House of Lords agreed by a majority of 3 to 2 (though the Court of Appeal disagreed) that as the medical practitioner remained in charge of the 'team' it was a termination by a medical practitioner for the purpose of the Act. Everyone involved recognised that it would be very beneficial to have a ruling by a court on what was clearly a very difficult legal issue. I obliged. However, I mentioned in my judgement that this was a novel use of a declaration and I granted the declaration although until someone attempted to prosecute a nurse, the issue was technically hypothetical.

It was on this peg that Mrs Gillick initiated her proceedings [*Gillick v West Norfolk Health authority* [1986] AC 112 [1984] QB 581] challenging the legality of a DHSS circular setting out the circumstances in which it was in order for a medical practitioner to provide children under the age of 16 with advice on the use of contraceptives without the agreement of the parents of the child. No one was seeking to take any action against any doctor but there is no doubt that the appropriateness of the giving of such medical advice was highly controversial. Mrs Gillick suggested that she was much concerned (as a mother, when the action commenced of 4, and by the time it concluded, of 5, daughters under 16) as to whether such advice was lawful. Again I granted a declaration that it was lawful to give such advice. If I was also suggesting that it was ethical to do so, I did not say so directly. Again the Court of Appeal disagreed. The Court of Appeal unanimously held that if a doctor were to treat a girl under 16 without parental consent, this would infringe the legal rights of the parents. The House of Lords allowed the appeal by a majority of 3 to 2.

The decision's greatest significance was probably the light it threw on the relationship between teenage children and their parents. Here I believe the case was constructive because the House of Lords (particularly Lord Scarman) did not deal with the issue in black and white terms. Instead the issue was described as a situation where the responsibility of the parents, and therefore their power to intervene reduced with the increasing ability of the child to take responsibility for their own actions.

The case also had a religious dimension because Mrs Gillick was a Roman Catholic. This undoubtedly influenced her attitude to education as to the provision of contraceptives to teenagers. From a medical point of view, the significance of the case was that it made clear that the courts were prepared to take responsibility for making pronouncements as to what should be the general approach by the medical profession to an ethical issue. In this respect, the case was very different from the decision in the Royal College of Nursing case. In the Gillick case, there was no statute which stated when it was and was not lawful for a doctor to take the action to which Mrs Gillick objected. Accordingly, the Court had to determine what was the appropriate standard. On the other hand the Royal College of Nursing's complaint was that the Department was requiring nurses to treat patients in a manner which contravened the Abortion Act.

The next case of interest is the *Attorney General v Able* [1984] QB 795. It constituted approval of the new advisory role of the courts. The Attorney General sought the court's advice as to whether the provision of pamphlets at the request of an individual regarding how to take your own life constituted aiding and abetting suicide, a criminal offence, if the recipient followed the pamphlet's advice. Ironically, I refused the plea of the Attorney General that the conduct was unlawful. To do so would amount to a finding that Mr Able had committed a criminal offence and it seemed to me that only a jury should perform that task. There was no appeal.

Those three cases covered contraception, abortion and euthanasia and as you would expect Lord Jakobovits dealt with each subject, not only from the perspective of Jewish Law but from that of the Greeks, the Romans, Islam and Christianity as well. The approach of Jewish Law is one with which I am perfectly comfortable. It is pragmatic and has much of the spirit of the common law, with a strong bias in favour of the procreation and preservation of human life. For example, so far as abortion is concerned, Lord Jakobovits states:

(182) In Jewish Law, the right to destroy a human fruit before birth is entirely unrelated to theological considerations. Neither the question of the entry of the soul before birth nor the claim to salvation after death has any practical bearing on the subject. *op. cit.*

The unborn child is protected through the protection provided by Jewish law for the mother.

Again, while Lord Jakobovits was understandably extremely concerned about the effect that the pill could have on morals and recognised its contribution to the permissive society, he emphasised that the approach of Jewish Law was extremely 'lenient.' The fact is, (as he pointed out in the second edition of his book), until his work on the subject the very term 'Jewish Medical Ethics' was unknown. Religious rulings on medical practices were concerned with their legality not their morality.

In this respect it appears to me that the Jewish approach could be said to be that of the law in this country. English law has for good reason traditionally eschewed becoming involved in issues of medical ethics. Wherever possible, the courts have left it to the medical profession to set their own standards as to what is appropriate practice. The Bolam test meant that a medical practitioner would not be guilty of negligence if he had acted in a manner which was regarded as acceptable by a respectable body of medical opinion.[4]

Again, no treatment can be given without the patient but what is a patient required to be told before he gives his consent?

The leading case in England is still *Sidaway v Royal Bethlehem Hospital*,[5] a 1985 decision of the House of Lords. The speeches in that case need to be read in full because their Lordships gave different views on a number of points. But setting aside the differences of opinion, it is fair to say that the majority thought that complaints about inadequate disclosure of the risks of treatment should be resolved through the application of the Bolam test. That is to say, in anything but exceptional circumstances a patient is only entitled to be told as much as a responsible body of medical opinion judges to be prudent. I say that there might be exceptional circumstances because Lord Bridge thought that there might be cases where disclosure of a particular risk was so necessary to an informed choice that it would have to be disclosed whatever the actual medical opinion might be. In practice, however, the case has come to mean that patients are entitled to know no more than what their doctors think they should know.[6]

In Canada, a different course was adopted in *Reibl v Hughes*.[7] That case directs attention not to what a reasonable doctor would disclose judged by the standards of his profession, but rather to what a reasonable patient would want to know. Laskin CJC held that doctors are under a duty to ensure that their patients receive the information they need to give an informed consent to surgical and other health care decisions. In particular, the physicians must discuss with their patients the nature of their illness and of the recommended treatment, disclose the material risks involved in that course of action, and discuss any alternatives as well as the consequences of doing nothing. A failure to give adequate information is actionable in negligence.

The Supreme Court of Canada has recently revisited the question of informed consent in *Arndt v Smith*.[8] In that case the court was invited to go further. It was urged that the doctor should disclose the risks that the particular patient, subjectively, wanted to know about but rightly confirmed Laskin CJC's 'modified objective test', which takes the question from the point of view of a reasonable patient in this patient's particular situation.

In a 1992 case, *Rogers v Whitaker*,[9] the Australian High Court also rejected the approach in *Sidaway* and chose to follow Canada. The court also opted for a mixed objective and subjective approach; the extent of the requirement of disclosure will depend in Australia on the extent of which a particular patient demonstrates an interest in being told. Since *Rogers v Whitaker* was decided, New South Wales has held in *Lowns v Woods*[10] that the Bolam test is not only the wrong test where disclosure of risk is concerned but it is also the wrong test in relation to decisions concerning treatment and diagnosis.

The difference between the two approaches is significant. In Canada and Australia, it is the courts, not the medical practitioners who are the final arbiters as to what medical ethics require a patient to be told. The decision in *Sidaway* has now to be read in light of the later decision of Bolitho.[11] Bolitho established that a doctor's decision not to disclose risks can be subjected to logical analysis by the courts. Thus if a doctor has withheld information that should have been disclosed without a good reason, then he will be liable even though his decision may have been consonant with ordinary professional practice. That was also my view in *Pearce v United Bristol Healthcare NHS Trust*,[12] which was decided last year. *Sidaway* has never been a popular decision. It endorses an objectionable form of medical paternalism. Moreover, it seems that whether a certain risk would or would not affect a patient's decision to undergo a course of treatment is not a question falling within the technical expertise of the medical profession. It allows the medical profession not only to set what is the ethical standard, but also the legal standard.

There appears to be a virtual consensus amongst academic commentators in England that *Sidaway*, at least as it has been understood, will need to be revised, perhaps in favour of the position that now obtains in both Canada and Australia.[13]

The advantage of leaving these issues to the medical profession is that they can speak with the benefit of great experience. It can be fairly asked what qualifications do judges have to determine these issues? The problem is that unless Parliament intervenes, courts have to try to hold the balance. Such is the pace of the advances in the frontiers of medical knowledge treatment and research that Parliament is unable to keep up. It was such phenomenal developments that explain why Lord Jakobovits felt it necessary to produce the second edition of his book in 1975. But over the last 25 years, the speed of developments has, if anything, increased. The result is that the courts are being asked to adjudicate on legal points that are bound up with fundamental and emotive questions of medical ethics with increasing frequency. In one area Parliament has acted in what I would suggest is a constructive manner. An area where there have been staggering advances is in the field of human fertilisation and embryology. In 1990 Parliament legislated by creating an Authority that was given wide licensing and supervisory powers. The Authority is an expert body and is ideally qualified to exercise the very delicate responsibilities it has been given. The establishment of the Authority does not, however, mean that the courts have no role to play. The Authority has great power and it is important therefore that the courts do not abdicate responsibility to ensure that bodies such as these exercise their responsibilities in accordance with the law.[14]

This was what I like to believe we did in the case of Mrs Blood.[15] You will remember that her husband developed meningitis and died in a coma, but a specimen of his sperm had been obtained before he died. The question was whether Mrs Blood was entitled to use that specimen so that she could have her deceased husband's child. It was not in dispute that prior to his death, the husband had agreed to this but he had failed so to state in writing as the Authority required. The Authority maintained that there was no reason to depart from the general rule. By a process of reasoning which it is not necessary to examine since Mrs Blood's situation should not arise again,[16] we were able to hold that as long as Mrs Blood had the treatment in Belgium, there was no objection in law to her taking the specimen abroad. This she did and I am glad to say she now has a healthy child, the first photograph of whom has been presented to me. The significance of the case is that it confirms what the Authority has always accepted; it is subject as a last resort to the supervision of the Court.

However, where such a body exists, the courts rarely become involved. Where there is no body equivalent to the Authority, then the declaratory jurisdiction of the court to which I referred earlier is still of the greatest importance. There are many grey areas as to what is or is not permissible or where there is a dispute, perhaps between the family and the doctors, as to what action should or should not be taken. As an example, consider *Airedale NHS Trust v Bland*[17] (the Tony Bland Case). The question was whether the hospital could lawfully discontinue life-sustaining treatment designed to keep alive a patient in a persistent vegetative state where there was no prospect of recovery. The House of Lords concluded that the doctors could discontinue the support measures. However, two members of the court, in eloquent terms, expressed their reservations about the propriety and suitability of judicial involvement in this process.

Undoubtedly, the most difficult case yet to come before the courts was that decided by the Court of Appeal on 22 September of last year. It involved the conjoined twins named Mary and Jodie.[18] You will remember that the unique feature of the case was that the girls shared a common aorta. That enabled Jodie, the stronger twin, to pump the blood she oxygenated through Mary's body. Mary would not have survived birth but for the support she received from Jodie. Worse still, Jodie's heart would not be strong enough to sustain both herself and her sister as they grew, and the estimates were that kept together, they had a life expectancy of 3–6 months. If they were separated, as the doctors felt they could be with good prospects of success, Mary would undoubtedly die but Jodie would probably be able to live a fairly normal life. The doctors saw an opportunity to save one of the girls and wished to separate the twins. The girls' parents, on the other hand, devout Roman Catholics who believed in the sanctity of life, loved their daughters equally and would not consent to a procedure that would kill one of them. The parents were resigned to letting nature take its course, as they felt it was God's will. The medical team sought a declaration from the court authorising them to separate the twins.

The judgments make clear that the trial judge, as well as the three Lords Justices who heard the appeal, found the case to be a very painful one. In spite of the acute pressures of time, the judgments are very long. In the event, all of the judges concluded that a declaration should be issued which authorised the separation of the twins.

These cases, and in particular the twins case, raise a number of difficulties for the courts, ranging from the practical problem of expeditiously resolving cases that tend to have a very short shelf life, to philosophical issues of medical ethics The timescale in which the cases are decided show that the courts can and will act with the necessary expedition. I do not propose to venture answers on any of the deeper philosophical questions in this area, but I will say something about the role of the courts in deciding these cases and the approach that should be adopted.

The twins case demonstrates how, in arriving at their conclusions, the Lords Justices had to traverse medical law principles concerning consent to treatment; family law principles regulating the parents' right to refuse consent to treatment of their children and questions about child welfare; the criminal law of murder; and finally the effect of the Human Rights Act 1998. Plainly these are questions that are properly decided by the courts.

Ward LJ stressed at the outset of his judgment that the court was a court of law and not a court of morals and that the duty of the court was to decide the case in accordance with the relevant principles of law. In a sense that is entirely right, but we cannot close our eyes to the fact that these legal questions are intertwined with ethical problems of a fundamental character. These are matters on which reasonable people can and do disagree. To the extent that this is so, the legitimacy of the judicial role may inevitably be questioned, for reasons famously given by Justice Scalia in *Cruzan v Director, Missouri Department or Health:*[19]

> The point at which life becomes 'worthless', and the point at which the means necessary to preserve it become 'extraordinary' or 'inappropriate', are neither set forth in the constitution nor known to the nine Justices of this Court any better than they are known to nine people picked at random from the Kansas City telephone directory.

While judges often have no better moral compass than other members of society, I think there are good reasons why questions with a fundamental ethical dimension should, in appropriate cases, be resolved in court quite apart from the fact that, when all is said and done, answers need to be given on points of law. Put differently, I do not think the fact that these cases have an ethical dimension is a reason for the courts to shy away from them when Parliament refuses to step in. Judicial proceedings allow ethical questions to be treated in a thorough and neutral fashion. Answers can be given which, whether right of wrong, have a fair degree of finality and legitimacy.

The finality and clarity of a judicial decision are of considerable importance where time is short and people need to be able to know how to proceed. Ward LJ said in the conjoined twins' case that the medical team 'could not proceed in the absence of parental consent. The only arbiter of that sincerely held difference of opinion is the court. Deciding disputed matters of life and death is surely and pre-eminently a matter for a court of law to judge'. He did not say, however, that the hospital had been under a duty to refer the question to the court. Ward LJ would not have criticised the medical team if it had decided to bow to the wishes of the parents and let nature take its course. But he said the medical team could also not be criticised for wishing to save the stronger twin and for having referred the legality of doing so to the court.

A second reason for treating questions with ethical dimensions in the courts is that judicial procedures have been carefully designed to allow discussion of contested questions to be pursued in an orderly, rational and thorough fashion with proper attention to the arguments on both sides. A third reason is that judicial proceedings are conducted in public. This is especially important if the answer is to have the legitimacy that it needs. Dissenters must see that their views have at least been aired and considered. A fourth reason is that judges are especially experienced in hearing all sides of a case with an open mind, analysing the issues and then giving a decision with impartiality. Moreover, while it is true that ethical questions raise special problems, the pattern of ethical argument is not so different from the familiar pattern of legal argument. Lord Justice Robert Walker noted one aspect of this in the conjoined twins' case, saying that 'in law as in ethics it is often necessary to consider the facts of the particular case, including relevant intentions, in order to form a sound judgment'.

Interestingly in the USA, an orthodox Jewish couple were faced with the same problem and obtained the same decision from their courts. However the case never received the same attention. This was no doubt because there was no dispute as to what the result should be. Rabbi Finestien, another expert in the field of Jewish ethics, justified one child being sacrificed to save another in Jewish law by citing a number of illustrations. The one I prefer, is that of two parachuters jumping out of a plane and one parachute not opening. The person without the parachute grabs the person with the parachute. Unfortunately, the single parachute is not strong enough to support both people and they hurtle to the ground. In that situation, according to Jewish law it is the duty of the man with the parachute to save his own life. For this purpose he is justified in sending his companion to his death. This is a pragmatic rather than gallant approach. The Rabbi would say Mary was in the same position as the person with the failed parachute. She was seeking to hold on to her sister who had the effective parachute and by so doing threatened to kill her.

There is however no question of courts breaching the right of a parent by requiring that she take action which she does not wish to take in order to protect her unborn child. A court did come to the contrary conclusion but the decision was resolutely condemned by academic writers. The courts have subsequently held that there can be no question of the interests of the unborn child resulting in an order that the mother has to undergo a Caesarean delivery against her will.

I do not intend these remarks as a counsel of complacency for judges. Archbishop Carey addressing the Royal College of Surgeons recently stressed the need for the medical profession to display humility in relation to the heavy responsibilities which the advances of science have placed upon them. Lord Jakobovits made similar comments directed to his rabbinic colleagues in Israel. In particular, he called for greater trust and understanding on both sides of the divide which he recognised existed between them. In deciding fundamental questions, judges as much as surgeons must exercise humility. In my experience, they do so. Neither medical nor legal qualifications depend upon good marks in a test on moral wisdom.

If the courts are to provide a satisfactory forum in which cases involving fundamental questions can be adjudicated, we need to pay close attention to whether we can improve on the manner in which we perform our role in hearing cases with fundamental ethical and spiritual dimensions.

Perhaps judges need to be prepared to listen to evidence of a different nature than that to which we are accustomed. Of course, judges always listen to what is being said in court, but listening has a special significance in the cases with which I am presently concerned. Listening serves two purposes. The first is that it leads to better-informed decisions. This has particular salience in cases that raise complicated questions of public morality, on which there may be several different perspectives. A defensible decision must proceed from a real appreciation of the force of those perspectives. The second reason, which is sometimes overlooked, is that listening serves to legitimise the eventual decision. The losers of a case, as well as the dissenting sections of the public, will be more inclined to respect the decision if they feel that their views have been patiently heard and carefully considered.[20]

The need for judges to listen prompts the next question. To whom should judges listen? In England, this question has traditionally received a very narrow answer. Of course, the most important people to listen to are the patient, their family, and the medical professionals involved. These are the people who are most immediately affected by the decision, and these are the people who have been turning the problem over most vigorously in their minds. I also think, however, that there are cases which raise points of general public concern on which the views of different sections of the public may not be properly represented by the parties to the particular action. In medical cases, it seems peculiarly appropriate to hear from the spiritual leaders of one or other faiths. Where children are concerned, it might be appropriate to hear from bodies with particular experience in child matters. Many examples suggest themselves.

This brings me back to procedure, and in particular, public interest intervention. By public interest intervention, I mean intervention by a third party who is not directly affected by a proceeding on the ground of an interest in the larger legal questions that are to be decided. Public interest intervention is quite uncommon in England, and we may have something to learn here from Canada. The Supreme Court of Canada has been allowing public interest interventions since at least 1963 when the Lord's Day Alliance of Canada intervened in *Robertson and Rosetanni v The Queen*.[21] The reception which public interest intervenors have experienced in that court has varied over time, and intervenors are rarely granted leave to make oral submissions. Nonetheless, public interest intervention is an established feature of Canadian Supreme Court practice. Interventions are also a regular feature of public law litigation in the provincial courts, although I understand that the rules differ from province to province.

The House of Lords does consider petitions for leave to intervene, but leave has only been granted in a small number of cases, the best known of these being Amnesty International's intervention in the *Pinochet* case.[22] I am not aware of any medical case before the House in which intervenors have been allowed. Certainly the House refused to permit the Children's Legal Centre to intervene in *Gillick v West Norfolk Area Health Authority*[†] after objection by counsel for one of the parties. The House has been moving

---

[†] See page 3 above [1986] AC 112.

towards a more liberal practice since that case was decided in 1980. The Human Rights Act has acted as a catalyst.

It is possible to intervene in proceedings before the English Court of Appeal, and even the High Court, but this is still unusual.[18] This was not a matter within the remit of my Access to Justice Inquiry.[23] The conjoined twin case itself, however, provides one example of a case in which intervention has been allowed. In that case, the Court of Appeal allowed both the Archbishop of Westminster and the Pro Life Alliance to make written submissions on the questions raised in the case. It was entirely appropriate that the Archbishop of Westminster should have been allowed to participate, as the parents of the twins are devout Catholics and this assisted in the judges understanding their position. We know that the judges found the Archbishop's submissions helpful because they were discussed in the course of the judgments. Nevertheless, it is clear that a balance must be observed because interventions undoubtedly increase expense and can give rise to delay.[24]

A balance must also be struck when determining the weight to be attached to the intervention. In general, the courts do not distinguish between the validity of the beliefs of one religion as against another unless the tenets are obnoxious or immoral by the norms of this country. This does not mean that cases must be decided according to the religious beliefs of those involved. In the case of children, in particular, the courts cannot abdicate their responsibility to decide cases in a manner which makes the welfare of the child the paramount consideration. A well-known quotation of Rutledge J. expresses the position admirably:

> Parents may be free to become martyrs themselves. But it does not follow that they are free, in identical circumstances, to make martyrs of children before they have reached the age of full and legal discretion and they can make choices for themselves.[25]

However, in a case such as that of the conjoined twins, the relevance of the parents' religion and the parents' wishes was a most powerful consideration and the court obviously needed all the help it could obtain in reaching its extremely difficult decision. My concern as onlooker was, what would happen if the parents rejected the surviving child. Fortunately, this did not occur and I was indeed pleased to read of the expression of pleasure of the parents at having a wonderful daughter at the end of the events in question.

That apparently happy ending, enables me to end, by recognising that the pioneering work of Lord Jakobovits is likely to continue to make a contribution of the greatest importance. His comparative approach to medical ethics is surely the way forward, in circumstances where courts are compelled to make difficult ethical decisions. Even with all possible help the decisions remain extraordinarily challenging. This is why they are so fascinating.

NOTES

[1] Jakobovits, I. (1959) *Jewish Medical Ethics* (New York, Bloch Publishing Company), p.154.

[2] *The Changing Relationship Between the Public and the Medical Profession* Donald Irvine JR Soc Med 2001; 94 162+169.

[3] *Royal College of Nursing v DHSS* [1981] 1 All ER 545.

[4] *Bolam v Friern Hospital Management Committee* [1957] 2 All ER 118.

[5] *Sidaway v Royal Bethlehem Hospital* [1985] 1 All ER 643.

[6] However, see *Chester v Afshar* [2004] UK HL.

[7] *Reibl v Hughes* (1980) 114 DLR.

[8] *Arndt v Smith* (1977) 148 DLR.

[9] *Rogers v Whitaker* [1992] 109 ALR 625.

[10] *Lowns v Woods* [1998] Med. L.R. 120 (NSWCA).

[11] In *Bolitho v City and Hackney Health Authority* (1997) & All ER 771 Lord Brown-Wilkinson stated that the court had to be satisfied that an opinion had to have a logical basis. In particular, in cases involving, as they so often do, the weighing of risks against benefits, the judge before accepting a body of opinion as being responsible, reasonable or respectable, will need to be satisfied that, in forming their views, the experts have directed their minds to the question of comparative risks and benefits and have reached a defensible conclusion on the matter.

[12] *Pearce v United Bristol Healthcare NHS Trust* (1999) 48 BMLR 118, CA.

[13] See *Chester v Afshar* [2004] UK HL.

[14] It is worth noting that in the Queen's Speech 2006, a Bill was proposed to unite the Human Fertilisation and Embryology Authority with the Human Tissue Authority: the Regulatory Authority for Tissue and Embryos, or in short, RATE.

[15] *R v HFEA ex p Blood* [1997] 2 All ER 627.

[16] However, see *Evans v Amicus Healthcare* [2004] EWCA Civ 727, a case which, at the time of going to press is awaiting a final decision by the ECJ.

[17] *Airdale NHS Trust v Bland* [1993] 1 All ER 821. HL.

[18] *Re A (Children) (Conjoined Twins: Separation)* [2001] Fam 147 CA.

[19] *Cruzan v Director, Missouri Department of Health* (1990) 110 S Ct 2841, 2859.

[20] On this point, see the contribution to this volume by Professor Sir Ian Kennedy.

[21] *Robertson and Roselanni v The Queen* [1963] SCR 651.

[22] *R v Bow Street Magistrates ex Pinochet* [1998] 3WLR 1456 (HL).

[23] *Access to Justice* Final Report by the Rt. Hon.The Lord Woolf, Master of the Rolls, 1996.

[24] Since the conjoined twins case, interveners were allowed in the Court of Appeal. See the case of *Burke v The General Medical Council* in the Court of Appeal [2005] EWCA 1003 July 2005. 'The British Section for the World Federation of Doctors Who Respected Human Life' and 'The Intensive Care Society' were allowed as 'interveners'.

[25] *Prince v Commonwealth of Massachusetts* (1944) 321 US 158 and see I.Kennedy and A.Grubb (Eds) *Principles of Medical Law* 1998

PUBLIC INQUIRIES: EXPERIENCE FROM THE BRISTOL PUBLIC INQUIRY[1]

The second lecture in the series, delivered on 7th February 2002 by Professor Sir Ian Kennedy[2]

ABSTRACT

The late Lord Jakobovits made immense contributions to medical ethics. His wisdom reminds us of our duty to constantly search for truth and understanding which makes us, whatever our religion, moral beings. The search for truth and understanding can be exemplified by Public Inquiries. This paper makes some general observations of the need for a Public Inquiry and how it might be conducted but it is largely based on experience of chairing the Public Inquiry into the conduct of children's heart surgery at the Bristol Royal Infirmary between 1984 and 1995.

The Bristol Inquiry was established by government as an independent Public Inquiry. It needed careful choice of Chair, sitting with other equal members to provide an appropriate range of expertise. There was no prior handbook or model on which to base how to proceed. The terms of reference, the response to concerns, the goals, the degree of flexibility all needed to be well planned in advance between the Chair and Government. It was important that all understood that, the primary aim was not to apportion blame. The purposes of the Inquiry needed to be stated clearly. These were to: discover the truth, achieve catharsis, hold people or organizations to account, begin healing, provide learning for the future, and to prescribe what should be done in the light of the findings. The overall aims were to facilitate understanding and to examine systems and how organizations work and not, as in a Court of Law, to attach responsibility or blame to individuals. It was also important that the Inquiry gave value for money and moved with all possible speed.

To meet these aims the Inquiry devised a set of guiding principles, foremost among which was rigour in obtaining evidence. Witnesses were called by the Inquiry, not on behalf of any individual. Evidence was heard directly from witnesses rather than through legal representatives. There was immense work needed to ensure that all relevant individuals were able to give written statements, with a selection of those to appear personally before the Inquiry. A team with appropriate skills and the best possible talent had to be created. These included legal advisors and individual experts in such matters as communications, information technology and statistics; also research staff and counsellors for bereaved families.

The Inquiry needed to be completely open so that everyone could see and hear the same evidence. This was achieved by the use of IT with scanning of all documents: this came to over 900,000 pages. A 'Core Bundle' of relevant documents was prepared as a CD available to all legal representatives. The daily proceedings could be seen at three separate locations as well as Bristol. It was also vital to create a website (this received over 1 million hits during the Inquiry and won a prestigious NHS prize).

Accessibility was achieved through choice of location, an office block, not a Town Hall or courtroom, with open arrangements for the public and media. The Inquiry also had to be fair – written statements were provided in advance by all witnesses and those mentioned in these statements were able to comment in advance also in writing. The Counsel to the Inquiry asked all the questions in an inquisitorial rather than adversarial fashion and, although cross examination by individual legal representatives could have taken place in certain circumstances, it was never needed.

The Inquiry sought to meet the needs of the patients and families, legal representatives, the media the Government and other interested groups, e.g. professional bodies. The aim was, however, to report to the public, albeit through the Secretary of State. The Inquiry was not to recommend financial compensation, disciplinary action or criminal actions but to recommend action to avoid future such occurrences.

The Inquiry lasted two years and nine months, cost £14 million pounds and made 198 recommendations which, except for a handful, the Government accepted. It has had a significant impact on the shape of policy about healthcare over the past five years.

INTRODUCTION

This paper first emerged as a Lecture given at the Royal Free Hospital in London on 7 February 2002, in honour of the late Lord Jakobovits.[3] I knew Immanuel Jakobovits and had benefited greatly from his advice and wise counsel. His particular interest in medical ethics (it was the subject of his doctoral dissertation) brought us together. I had the privilege of working with him and of being entertained in his home. We worked together for a number of years in a group formed at King's College London to discuss medical ethics. The group brought together Protestants, Catholics, Jews – and lost souls such as me. I learned to admire Immanuel not only for his wisdom and erudition, but also for his kindness and enthusiasm for intellectual challenge and debate.

There is a story attributed to Lord Jakobovits which goes as follows. Three men, doomed by their doctors to die within 3 months, were asked how they would spend the time left to them. The Scotsman answered that he would cheerfully squander his savings on all the pleasures which he had previously denied himself. The Frenchman spoke of the utter abandon with which he would dine and wine to his heart's content. And the Jew simply said, 'I would look for another doctor to get a second opinion'. As Lord Jakobovits explained, this story illustrates the perennial refusal of the Jew to regard anything as final or inevitable. This has meant that even in the darkest days, when Jewry was threatened with doom, the Jew, refusing to accept finality, has consulted his faith for a second opinion.

The gloss that I would put on the story is that it reminds us of our duty constantly to search for truth and understanding; a duty which marks us out as moral beings, whether Jew, Christian, Muslim, Hindu, or whatever. That is what the Bristol Inquiry, in its small way, was about.

After the Jakobovits Lecture, I dedicated my Presidential address to the Bentham Club in the following month[4] to the same subject. In December, 2004, I gave evidence to the House of Commons' Select Committee on Public Administration, as part of its examination of Public Inquiries.[5] In this paper, I draw on all of these.

Bristol

From 1998 until 2001, I chaired the Public Inquiry into the conduct of children's heart surgery at the Bristol Royal Infirmary between 1984−95. The Report of the Inquiry was published as *Learning from Bristol*, (2001).[6]

The establishment of the Inquiry was announced in Parliament by the then Secretary of State for Health, Frank Dobson, on 18 June 1998. As Chairman, I sat with three others.[7] The first formal, public hearing was on 27 October 1998, when I set out the procedures that the Inquiry would follow. The hearings in public began on 16 March 1999 and ended with the final submissions from interested parties on 9 February 2000. The final Report of the Inquiry was published in July, 2001, a separate Report having been published in May, 2000.

BACKGROUND

In this paper, I seek to make some general observations about the circumstances which might determine whether to establish a Public Inquiry and how it might be conducted. In 2005, Parliament passed the Inquiries Act. Given the very general nature of its terms, I am persuaded that the views expressed here remain worthy of exploration.

Inquiries which are the subject of this paper come in many shapes and sizes. They effectively defy characterization, in that they are:

- creatures of Government at the whim of government, usually central government. I will not be examining inquiries set up, for example, by local authorities or local hospital trusts, although some of the points made may apply;

- statutory (derived from a specific statute) or non-statutory;
- public or private;
- widely variable in terms of –
    terms of reference,
    subject matter,
    perspective (e.g. that of the public, the consumer, the patient, the taxpayer).

A STARTING POINT

The first question that requires attention is whether there are some issues which should be the subject of a Public Inquiry, all other things being equal, and some that should not be. This question is pertinent because of recent events in the UK. The suicide of Dr David Kelly, a scientist who specialized in biological and chemical warfare, prompted the Government to set up a Public Inquiry, under Lord Hutton. The basis of the British government's decision to go to war against Iraq, though not the subject of the Inquiry, inevitably formed the backdrop.[8] To some, Lord Hutton's Report was a vindication. To others, it was a 'whitewash'. The subsequent Report of the Inquiry by Lord Butler into other aspects of the circumstances surrounding the decision to go to war suffered a similar fate.[9] Clearly, those with fixed views were not to be moved by forensic examination of evidence. More important, in terms of the general good of the body politic, a distinguished judge became to some, overnight, a 'lackey of Government', and a distinguished public servant was praised or reviled, not by reference to what he had said, but whether he was seen to be 'for' or 'against' the Prime Minister. Respect for and belief in a particular constitutional mechanism, the public inquiry, were put at risk, not because of the merits or otherwise of the mechanism, but solely based on whether the answer arrived at was the 'right' one.

A Distinction between two types of issue

In the light of this recent experience, I would propose that it may be plausible and helpful to draw a distinction between two types of issue. The distinction is not, perhaps, clearly delineated. Indeed, it may be more helpful to talk in terms of a spectrum of issues, some falling largely towards one end and others towards the other. But, that said, there is, I submit, a distinction which can be made between:

- those issues that directly involve the action or inaction of government, present or past, which I will call TYPE A; and

- those that do not directly involve the action or inaction of government, which I will call TYPE B.

TYPE A

Recent examples of this type would include the Inquiries carried out by Sir Richard Scott, and those just mentioned, conducted by Lords Hutton and Butler. In this sort of case, my view is that the establishment of a Public Inquiry is not the right approach. No matter who is appointed to chair the Inquiry, the political nature of the issue means that some, from the outset, will never accept the Inquiry's findings, as a matter of party politics, whatever evidence is adduced. The Inquiry, and the Chair's role in it, is impossibly compromised from the beginning. The situation is even worse if the Inquiry is chaired by a senior judge. Not only will the judge as Chair be compromised from the outset, but, given the nature of the issues under consideration, s/he will, at the same time, inevitably have been drawn into the party political arena. As a consequence, judicial independence, both in theory and in practice, will be seriously undermined.

In my view, the only forum in which issues of this type can properly be examined is Parliament. It is for Parliament itself to deal with them. That its current procedures do not allow it to do so effectively does not serve as a reason for passing what is ultimately a political responsibility elsewhere. Rather, it casts on Parliament the duty so to revise its procedures that it can examine the type of issue under consideration. After all, by doing so, it would be doing no more than carrying out one of its principal roles, subjecting Government to public scrutiny.

TYPE B

Recent examples of this type would include such Inquiries as Lawrence,[11] Paddington,[12] Bristol,[13] and Shipman.[14] The Inquiry into BSE[15] may be said to sit in the middle of the proposed spectrum, since it concerned the conduct of departments of State, but its remit went significantly beyond the actions and inactions of the Departments involved.

My position is that it is on issues falling under Type B that the discussion of the merits of and justification for Public Inquiries should focus. Consequently, I shall concentrate on Type B in what follows.

CRITERIA FOR ESTABLISHING A PUBLIC INQUIRY

To the person seeking a guide to the circumstances in which a Public Inquiry should be set up, the first point of reference would naturally seem to be to some formal criteria. Indeed, if they existed, the previous discussion about types of Inquiry would have been unnecessary. In fact, however, very few criteria exist and, where they do, they tend to be very general. They are to be found in the few cases which have come before the courts in which the issue has been addressed, in the writings of academics, and in the Bristol Report itself:

- Public confidence and trust in government or a public service cannot otherwise be restored (*Bristol*, *Walshe* (Walshe, K., Higgins, J., 'The use and impact of inquiries in the NHS', (2002) *British Medical Journal* 325; 895–900).
- The integrity of the system of justice is under challenge (*R v SoS for EFRA, ex p Persey* [2003]).
- Misfeasance by government (*Persey*).
- A major disaster with loss of many lives (*R v SoS for Health, ex p Wagstaffe* [2002], *Walshe*).
- An issue of significant importance is involved which also raises matters of wider public concern (*Bristol*).
- A Public Inquiry will bring added value, i.e. the issue cannot be examined as appropriately in any other way that is less expensive, less elaborate, and more speedy (*Bristol*).
- New or poorly understood issues of major public concern are involved (*Walshe*).

APPLYING THE CRITERIA – DECIDING ON A PUBLIC INQUIRY

If Public Inquiries of the sort that I am discussing are the creatures of government, then, clearly, it is government, in one form or another which decides whether to set up a Public Inquiry. The important question, of course, is what persuades government to do so. It will be obvious from the criteria just set out that there are no rules, or even guidelines, to which government can be held accountable, or must follow. The reality is that Public Inquiries quite clearly live in the world of politics. It is quintessentially a political decision to set one up: a decision born of the political calculation that there is something to be gained and more to be lost by not doing so. Talk of guidelines or rules, therefore, misses the point. What is important is political pressure and political calculation. Section 1 of the Inquiries Act, 2005, makes this poignantly clear by purporting to legislate on the circumstances in which an Inquiry may be set up and giving up immediately. The section reads:

> 1(1) A Minister may cause an inquiry to be held under this Act in relation to a case where it appears to him that –
> (a) particular events have caused, or are capable of causing, public concern, or
> (b) there is public concern that particular events may have occurred.

THE CHAIR

The first step, once it has been decided to hold a Public Inquiry, is to appoint a Chair. S/he will, thereafter, need to be involved in all that follows, from framing the terms of reference onwards. The appointment of the Chair will ordinarily condition the way in which the Inquiry is both perceived and how it is conducted. Thus, it is a very important decision. Ultimately, it is a matter for the Secretary of State or Minister whose Department is establishing the Inquiry.

The person appointed must be of sufficient standing and have sufficient experience of and expertise in the subject matter of the Inquiry to command the respect of all those affected by it. Furthermore, s/he must understand issues of procedural fairness and due process and what constitutes evidence. This suggests a background in law.

Should the Chair sit alone? I have no doubt that the Chair should sit with others, perhaps two or three, who bring necessary additional skills and background. The reasons are obvious. No Chair can be the repository of all knowledge and wisdom. There is everything to gain from collective debate and discussion, particularly when the issues at stake are both complex and highly charged. Moreover, collective decision-making makes it less easy for those unhappy with the Inquiry or its findings to attack the person of the Chair, rather than address what the Inquiry finds or recommends.

If, as I would urge, the Chair always sits with others, the status of those others must be agreed at the outset. There are two options: they can be advisers to the Chair or full members, with an equal say in the conduct and outcome of the Inquiry. Which of these options is the more appropriate will depend on a number of factors. Certainly, my view is that, if it is thought that the Inquiry will last for more than a few months, those sitting with the Chair should ordinarily be equal members. It seems to me unreasonable to expect them to give large amounts of their time, yet remain only advisers, whose views can be discarded at the Chair's say-so.

While discussing the role of Chair, I would add one further point on which I feel strongly. In my view, the Chair of a Public Inquiry should not be a sitting judge. The reasons are two-fold. The first is of some constitutional importance. Judges are seen and expected to be independent of other branches of government. To involve them in the chairing of Public Inquiries, usually into matters of considerable public and often political disagreement, is to risk bringing their independence into question. This is the more so because, as a necessary feature of the conduct of a Public Inquiry, they cannot call on the authority and respect which they can claim in the conduct of legal cases, surrounded as these are by rules and precedents and the possibility of appeal.

The second reason is of a different order. Judges have spent their lives in courtrooms. They see issues in binary terms, as being right or wrong, true or false. They are used to and rely upon a set of procedures at the heart of which is the proposition that there is a single truth and that it can be elicited by the application of forensic skill. Examination and cross-examination by counsel are what they are used to. Whatever the suitability of this approach, or what lies behind it, to the conduct of a Public Inquiry, this is how Public Inquiries conducted by judges tend to turn out. The Public Inquiry becomes a court of law. And, as I will hope to show in a moment, this is precisely what Public Inquiries should not be. Courts of law and the procedural approach associated with them lack the subtlety and sensitivity required of a Public Inquiry. Judges, only really at home in courts, equally, therefore, do not naturally bring to a Public Inquiry the range of skills required.[16]

TERMS OF REFERENCE

The terms of reference of an Inquiry have an elusive quality. They set the terms of the Inquiry, yet, at the same time, they may well serve only as a signpost to where the Inquiry will go. This elusiveness is easy to understand. The terms are the first step in getting the Inquiry on its way. They reflect the concerns which gave rise to the Inquiry and the goals which are hoped for. But they are necessarily the product of only partial understanding; after all, the Inquiry has not yet begun, and when it does, the evidence may lead in a variety of directions, only some of which could have been predicted. So, the terms must retain for the Inquiry a degree of flexibility. They should not be too restrictive. But, flexibility holds dangers either for Government, or for the Inquiry. The Government does not want the Inquiry rampaging about, turning over every stone it comes across. The Inquiry does not want to be stuck with an impossible task, or one which would take a decade to do properly.

The answer lies in careful thought and even careful drafting. The answer also lies in the close engagement of the Chair. While, on the face of things, the terms are for Government, they must be acceptable to the Chair, who will, after all, have to do the work. The Chair must, of course, understand and accept the broad sweep of Government's ambitions for the Inquiry. But, the Chair must also ensure that the Inquiry has a degree of room for manoeuvre which will allow the Inquiry to respond to the story as it unfolds. Of course, both Government and Chair can agree on narrow terms and then stick to them. But, this often ends in tears, with the Chair having to defend a report or recommendations which seem limited by saying that 'I was not asked to look at this', or 'that was outside my terms of reference'. This is not a satisfactory outcome, least of all for the taxpayer who will have footed the bill.

WHAT ARE PUBLIC INQUIRIES FOR?

My Approach

Here I am concerned to explore perhaps the question which is, at the same time, the most important, yet one of the least examined. Public Inquiries must serve some purpose. What is that purpose (or are there more than one)? And, equally important, is the purpose unique to Public Inquiries, because, if it is not, alternative ways of meeting the purpose warrant consideration?

In what follows, I draw on the approach that I adopted in the case of the Bristol Inquiry.

Background to Bristol

First, it may help if I set out very briefly what Bristol was about. The then Secretary of State for Health, Frank Dobson, announced to the House of Commons in July, 1998 that in the wake of the disciplinary hearings before the GMC and the representations of many parents, he had decided to establish a Public Inquiry into the conduct of paediatric cardiac surgery at Bristol Royal Infirmary during the years 1984 to 1995.

The Inquiry's terms of reference were: 'to inquire, make findings as to adequacy of care, reach conclusions concerning action taken', and '... to make recommendations to help to secure high quality care across the NHS'. This second part of the terms of reference meant that the Inquiry not only had to discover what went on in Bristol. It also had about as wide a brief as could be contemplated to apply what it learned to reshaping the NHS. The breadth of this second mandate went far beyond what would normally be the case. Terms of reference ordinarily, if they call for recommendations at all, call for more focussed recommendations arising out of the particular circumstances under review. The challenge given to the Inquiry was intended. We were being asked to think about the future shape of the NHS and healthcare generally. Perhaps, Government did not predict how far we would cast the net, but we made it clear from the outset that we accepted the challenge and would be casting our net very widely.[17]

Next, the Inquiry was a Public Inquiry. It need not have been. The Secretary of State had a number of other options available. He could have ordered that an Inquiry be carried out in private by some outside figure, unconnected with Bristol, or even healthcare. This was a common response to calls for inquiries.[18] It was rejected in the case of Bristol, since it was clear that the parents with whom the Secretary of State was dealing, and those supporting them, had no confidence in anything carried out in private. They wanted everything to be in the public domain as a guarantee of accountability. For the sake of completeness, it was open to the Secretary of State to ask the Commission for Health Improvement,[19] or the relevant NHS trust (the United Bristol Hospital Trust) to conduct an investigation, or inquiry. Given the high profile that the events had gained, these were never serious options.

The fact that a Public Inquiry was chosen as the appropriate response had its consequences which this paper seeks to address and analyse.

PURPOSE(S)

What I had to ask myself is: what was I being asked to do. Once I was able to answer that question, I could then go on to deal with the second question: how was I going to do it. And, critically, in addressing these questions, I had to remind myself at all times that I was not being asked to be a judge, nor was I presiding over a court.

So, how did I answer the first question: what was I being asked to do? I took the view from the outset that a Public Inquiry, any Public Inquiry and not just the Bristol Inquiry, is intended to serve not one, but a number of purposes. Moreover, it was clear that achieving these purposes would be challenging, not least because they did not all complement each other. Indeed, meeting one might, unless carefully managed, mean failing to meet another.

The following were the purposes that I identified:

- Discovering 'the truth'.
- Achieving catharsis for those affected by the events in Bristol.
- Holding people and organisations to account.
- Beginning a process of healing.
- Learning for the future.
- Prescribing what should be done in the light of lessons learned.

Two other factors should be mentioned. Although they are not strictly purposes, they significantly condition all aspects of a Public Inquiry. They are:

- Value for money – given that public funds are being spent, the Inquiry must be conducted in the most cost-efficient and effective way
- All due speed – given that time means money, that those affected need an end to the burden that the events under inquiry and the Inquiry itself represent, and that government needs advice so as to introduce any necessary measures as soon as possible, the Inquiry must be conducted with all due speed.

Having set out these purposes in general terms, it may help if I examine each one in turn.

Discovering 'The Truth' or Establishing 'The Facts'

This purpose is both the most commonly cited and the most misleading. It is usually said, at the establishment of a Public Inquiry, that the Inquiry will 'get to the bottom of things'. Indeed, I gave this pledge myself. But, this must not be thought to be the same as 'discovering the truth'. The reason is simple, yet hard to grasp by those raised on the (spurious) certainty of a courtroom's black and white. In the examination of complex events, involving many people, over a long period of time, there are, in fact, many truths, not just one; many accounts, each which its own claim to validity. In the context of interactions between doctors and patients, what the patient heard may not be what the doctor said, but it is no less true for the patient. In a courtroom, where one 'party' has to 'win', such an approach cannot be admitted. In a Public Inquiry, where there are no 'parties', no 'winners' and it is understanding rather than a binary approach to reality that is important, the acceptance of multiple truths is a crucial first step.

Thus, discovering 'the truth' becomes discovering the layers of understanding and perception which prompted the actions and reactions of those involved. There may be circumstances in which it matters that, for example, a meeting was on a Friday rather than a Monday and that this can be established unequivocally. But, there will also be many circumstances in which recollections will differ and where the fact that they differ is more important than resolving the difference. This is a complex notion, alien to the instincts of those used to the courtroom. But, unless it is grasped, the Inquiry will founder at the first hurdle and will convert itself into a trial.

Even when there is a grudging acceptance of the notion of multiple truths, the pursuers of certainty, those who would discover 'the truth', will play what they see as a trump. They will refer to 'the documents'. My response is to say: 'beware of documents'. They introduce a dangerous air of certainty. In an urge to find something to rely on as 'fact', the fact that something has been written down and is regarded as a record, clearly seems to fit the bill. But, anyone who has had the slightest connection with the real world of how organisations, large and small, work, will tell you that the documents rarely, if ever, tell the whole story and sometimes tell you the wrong story. Decisions are made, deals struck, confidences passed on in corridors, offices, and lifts without any documentation. Nuances are negotiated; agreements are reached that the minutes were not intended to mean this or that; concessions are made and agreed as 'not for minuting'.

Documents provide an illusion of certainty. To rely on them exclusively as the (or even a) historical record of what may have been happening is to make a serious mistake. To give them some elevated status, as 'the best evidence', is equally a serious mistake. They are part of the story, but only part, and they belong in a context.

I have already referred to the way in which organizations work in practice. They are organic entities, with complex informal structures grafted onto and often more important than the formal. Discovering 'the truth' must take account of this complexity and structure. That a memorandum records something as agreed does not mean that everyone involved in fact agreed. That a memorandum was marked as circulated widely does not mean that it was read, or understood, by all those named. And so on.

One final point is worth making. It should be clear that I would replace 'Discovering 'the truth'' with 'Facilitating understanding' as more clearly reflecting the first purpose of an Inquiry. It follows that, in the conduct of an Inquiry, all of the evidence sought by the Inquiry, the questions it asks, the witnesses it hears from, must all be designed to achieve this end. In the case of Bristol, and I think it is generally the case, as I will explain more fully later, understanding was more likely to flow from examining the 'systems' underlying how the organization worked. This is the story, how the organisation works in all its complexity, which is the story that any Inquiry should concentrate on. This is the story which the Inquiry should focus on in the evidence it chooses to examine, because this will facilitate understanding. It is tempting to some, of course, to concentrate their attention on the behaviour of certain particular individuals and seek to explain everything in terms of their failings. But, chasing down some individuals who can be singled out will not facilitate understanding, though it may feed some atavistic appetite. By contrast, a recognition of the need to focus on 'systems', informed by the work of such pioneers of the analysis of failing organizations as Professor James Reason,[20] is of crucial importance. It was an absolutely crucial guide to the pursuit of understanding in the case of the Bristol Inquiry.

Catharsis

It is often overlooked in the forensic hurly-burly which attends the setting up of a Public Inquiry that the Inquiry is about people; people who have died, been injured or survive, and their families, friends and relatives. The psychological and emotional weight of the Inquiry, the memories it brings back, the hopes and despair it engenders, must never, for one moment, be forgotten by those conducting or involved in the Inquiry. The response must be to seek to create through the medium of the Inquiry the circumstances in which catharsis can take place. In the case of Bristol, this meant catharsis for individuals, for example, parents of children who had died and the doctors and nurses who had looked after them. It also meant catharsis for groups, such as the nursing and medical staff at the hospital, all of whom felt the shadow of the Inquiry hanging over them. And finally, it meant, if possible, catharsis for a whole community, since the events which gave rise to the Inquiry had traumatized the whole city of Bristol.

Catharsis, in my view, is a noble purpose for a Public Inquiry. It is a necessary step on the way to understanding. It has implicit in it an element of theatre. It allows the opportunity for feelings to be expressed. It licences expressions of sadness, of anger, of sorrow, and of happiness, in an environment and context in which such displays are not seen as being out of place. As will be seen, meeting this purpose significantly affected the way in which the Bristol Inquiry was conducted.

Accountability

It is a legitimate expectation and, thus, a proper purpose of a Public Inquiry that organizations and people should be held to account for the events which gave rise to the Inquiry. It is crucial, however, to have a clear understanding of what accountability means and what function it serves. In my view, accountability contemplates the existence of a system or set of principles and rules which are known by those regulated by them and by reference to which they are to be held account. It does not consist of some after-the-event attribution of blame, on the basis that something has gone wrong and someone ought to 'carry the can'. The function served by accountability is, of course, to affix responsibility where this can fairly be achieved. But, more important, its purpose is to contribute to an understanding of what happened and to seek thereby to prevent similar occurrences in the future, not least by devising mechanisms which will achieve this end. One such mechanism will, of course, be a proper system of accountability, by reference to which, all those in an organization will know what is expected of them, whom to report to, and by what criteria their performance will be judged.

This rather careful notion of accountability does not, of course, sit well with calls for heads to roll, nor with blaming the most readily identifiable or prominent individuals. In the case of Bristol, two doctors had been 'struck off' the medical register and another had had limitations placed on what he was allowed to do and then dismissed by the hospital which employed him.[21]

Here, therefore, were three ready-made candidates for blame and, in the views of some in the press and elsewhere, there might be more.

But blame is not a mechanism for systematically assuring and determining accountability. It is a serendipitous approach, picking out some individuals without reference to their interaction with others and to the context and systems within which they worked. It also profits from the perspective of hindsight, a perspective no fair system of accountability can adopt. That there may be individuals who should be blamed is a given in any Public Inquiry. But, it must also be a given that any blame flows from and is the consequence of a proper approach to accountability. It cannot be the starting point.

Once again, an understanding of what the purpose that I have called accountability really means significantly affected the way in which the Inquiry was conducted. The organization of the evidence was specifically choreographed, so that the Inquiry, and the public following it, could obtain as full an understanding as possible of the way in which the care of children with congenital heart defects was organized in the relevant period, before the surgeons and the doctor who was the chief executive of the hospital trust, who were heretofore the sole objects of obloquy, were called to give their evidence. In this way, there was a context. Accountability could properly be attributed to organizations and individuals against the background of the circumstances in which they worked.

I would add one further point. Blaming three or more individuals for what happened in Bristol might have satisfied some. It would not have achieved a great deal by way of understanding any underlying systemic problems. Nor would it have necessarily protected the lives of children, or other patients, in the future. The reason is obvious. Take the three or so individuals out of the hospital, covered in blame, and replace them with three others. The result will be that they will encounter some or all of the systemic difficulties faced by the previous three: in the case of Bristol, a situation in which care was split between two sites, too few cardiologists who were not available in the operating theatre, poor equipment, insufficient facilities in intensive care, shortages of trained nursing staff, poor arrangements for providing covering care at night, dysfunctional management and poor leadership. Unless these underlying issues were properly understood and addressed, the risk that the pattern of poor care would be repeated was high. Against that background, merely to blame three doctors, as if that would solve everything (or anything) can be seen to be a nonsense.

Healing

I have already said that catharsis may a first step on the way to healing. But, healing is also an end in itself: an important end or purpose. It should be recognized clearly as one of the principal goals of an Inquiry. However, it must be said that there is a real risk that an Inquiry will take too narrow a view of its role. It may simply see its function as being to hear and weigh the evidence, deliberate on its conclusions and recommendations, write its report, and then dissolve itself. To do so overlooks what is so obvious that it is easily overlooked.

For those touched by the Inquiry, their lives in one way or another have been irrevocably affected by it. When the Inquiry leaves town, they continue to live their lives. If those lives are lives in which they are shunned by others, or remain fixed in grief, or stuck in defence and denial, the Inquiry has failed them. This is because the Inquiry should seek to promote understanding. Part of that understanding is an understanding of how others may feel and why some may have done what they did. And with that understanding comes the possibility of healing. The Inquiry has a duty to seek to heal broken lives, so that there can be life after the Inquiry.

Learning

A central function of any Public Inquiry is to enable lessons to be learned. This is self-evident. Less evident is that lessons cannot be learned unless the Inquiry begins its inquiry with an open mind. Having a view at the outset of what the appropriate conclusions should be, therefore, is best avoided! Instead, the Inquiry must not be led to premature evaluations because of previous speculations, or even the findings of other bodies. Lines of enquiry should not be discounted or discouraged because they do not fit current assumptions. Everything is grist for the mill. This is a fundamental principle of fairness.

It might be objected that my earlier reference to adopting a 'systems' approach constituted a conclusion which the evidence was then made to fit, with the consequences that the lessons extracted were the wrong ones. My answer is that the 'systems' approach was adopted to prevent the too-early adoption of conclusions based crudely on blame. Blame was not excluded. It was merely considered after the evidence was assembled rather than conditioning what evidence would be assembled.

Prescribing

Once the lessons thrown up by the Inquiry have been extracted, the Inquiry has the function of prescribing, or making recommendations. The scale and scope of the recommendations may be set out in the terms of reference. It cannot be doubted, however, that recommendations should be made.[22] Government, having set up the Inquiry, is clearly interested in gaining as much benefit as possible from it, and one of the obvious benefits are recommendations for future action.

The Government does not, of course, have to accept the recommendations and will not do so if they fail to subscribe to some fairly obvious criteria. In my view, these are that any recommendations should be:

- Practical.
- Achievable.
- Understandable.
- Affordable.
- Modest.

Perhaps only the last of these warrants any explanation. By modest, I mean that an Inquiry should avoid recommendations in the form of some grand gesture or iconic statement. Recommending the appointment of some all-powerful 'Tsar' in the context of healthcare is, perhaps, a good example of something to avoid. A series of modest steps which can be readily put in place is usually to be preferred. This is without prejudice to mapping out a new architecture as the vision of where these modest steps should be leading. Such a vision is often essential. But, the recommendations should address how to get there not merely recommend that there is where we should be.

HOW TO MEET THESE PURPOSES?

If what I have set out above are the purposes to be served by a Public Inquiry, the next question is, how should the Inquiry set about meeting them.

In my view, there are two necessary steps. First, the Inquiry must adopt a set of guiding principles. Then, it must adopt an approach to the conduct of the Inquiry which translates these guiding principles into practice.

But, it might be asked, is there not a set of guidelines, or some sort of Manual, prepared by Government, setting out 'How to conduct a Public Inquiry'? Surely, it cannot be for the Chair to work it out for himself, with all the risks of getting it wrong that this may entail. The answer is that, at the time that I was asked to carry out the Bristol Inquiry, there was no such guidance. It was very much a matter of 'DIY (do it yourself)'. Clearly, this can be a little unnerving. It can also cause those in charge to take refuge in past practice, which may not readily transfer to current needs, or to the familiar, such as adopting the approach used by a court. As it happens, I found it entirely liberating. It meant that, having taken the counsel of wise colleagues, I could reflect carefully on what the Inquiry was there to achieve (which I have already set out) and then design an approach to meet these purposes.[23]

Guiding principles

The following seven principles guided the conduct of the Inquiry:

- rigour;
- openness;
- accessibility;
- accountability;
- fairness and appropriate procedure;
- serving different publics;
- explain what the Inquiry is *not* addressing.

In this next section, I will explain how the Inquiry addressed each of these. But, first, I need to emphasize that nothing can be achieved by way of translating principle into practice without the creation of the team which will be responsible for doing so. By 'team', I mean the senior members of staff who will manage the conduct of the Inquiry. Paraphrasing Mrs Beaton, 'First create your team'.

This involves the following steps:

- identify the Inquiry's needs. These may range from legal advice, to communications, to Information Technology, to statisticians, to researchers. The needs will vary over time and must be anticipated so that work is never held up while staff are recruited.
- recruit the best available talent. The system of recruitment should be transparent and open. The only criterion for selection should be the ability to do the job in question to the highest possible standards.
- encourage challenge and debate. The team must see itself as a team and work as one. Strategy, tactics and decisions should be discussed openly and vigorously. Decisions once taken should be adhered to. Delegation of responsibility and clear lines of reporting and accountability must be established from the outset.
- share the vision which informs the approach to the Inquiry. It is crucial that the team understands and feels part of the vision. They, in turn, can then ensure that every member of staff also feels part of it.

Reverting now to the principles that I just set out, the first is:

RIGOUR.

There is no short cut to understanding. In the case of Bristol, the Inquiry was concerned with a period of twelve years and with events which took place not only in the wards and operating theatres of a hospital in Bristol, but in places ranging from Whitehall to South Wales to Birmingham. The number of people who might conceivably be able to assist the Inquiry was very large.

In such circumstances, there is no alternative but to throw the net as wide as possible and slowly draw it in, selecting and discarding as you go. The watchword is rigour. The Inquiry must be rigorous in establishing what it wishes to know and in tracking down any information that may assist it in this process. Equally, the Inquiry must identify what it needs advice on and draw upon the best experts.

Let me describe, by way of illustration, how this principle was translated into practice in the Bristol Inquiry.

The best evidence

The process of gathering evidence took months before the Inquiry began its formal hearings. This process was crucial. It meant that the evidence could be analysed and areas of importance identified, so that the hearings could then focus on these areas in a structured and efficient manner. Around 900,000 pages of documents were scanned into the Inquiry's data-base. There were two principal sources. First, the medical care of 1800 children was scrutinized. This involved examining 2,056 medical records, amounting to 3,497 files, and a total of 673,963 pages. Secondly, 42,071 other documents were identified as relevant, drawn from 30 sources and amounting to 219,828 pages. The Inquiry continued to receive further evidence, right up until the end. It was assessed, and where relevant added to the material that the Inquiry took account of in reaching its conclusions.

The Inquiry wanted to hear from all who could help in reaching a view on the events at Bristol Royal Infirmary over the relevant period of time. Some were easy to identify: the parents of children with congenital heart defects who had been treated in Bristol; and members of the staff, (nurses, doctors and managers) who had been involved in their care. As the net was cast more widely, others were identified as being possible sources of information and insight.[24] To ensure that the Inquiry did not overlook anyone, calls for witnesses were issued through NHS organisations and a range of newspapers. The Inquiry even sought to identify every junior doctor and trainee who had worked in Bristol over the relevant period to understand what they had seen and heard during their few months spent there.

To ensure that the formal hearings conducted by the Inquiry were tightly focussed and addressed matters identified as being of significance, the Inquiry identified those witnesses whom it wished to hear from and those whose written evidence would suffice. Those witnesses who were to be called were required to prepare a Witness Statement. Appropriate advice was made available, either through legal advisers or through the Inquiry's own legal team, to enable the Statements to be drawn up. The Inquiry's lawyers then read each Statement and advised whether any reference to another person could reasonably be regarded as critical of that person. If it could, the Statement was sent to the person named, with the invitation to comment on what was said.

Clearly, this process called for careful planning, so as to avoid delays. The advantages were enormous. Crucially, the Inquiry proceeded on the basis of written evidence, rather than oral evidence. This encouraged greater focus and was much more efficient in terms of the time taken. Secondly, before a witness gave evidence, the Inquiry had had the opportunity to review the evidence and had been made aware of what might be contested. This allowed attention to be focussed where it was needed. Thirdly, and very importantly both for the process of the hearings and their tone, the existence of comments from those referred to in Statements meant that the Inquiry's counsel could put all the sides of any proposition to the witness, thus obviating the need for cross-examination by a phalanx of other lawyers. At a stroke, the Inquiry was confirmed as an Inquiry rather than a court of law.

The emphasis on rigour from the outset paid dividends. In what was called Phase 1 of the Inquiry, the Public Hearings lasted 9 months (96 days of actual hearings), during which time the Inquiry heard from 577 witnesses, including 238 parents.

The best advice

The Inquiry recognized the need to be advised on a range of issues by the best experts. The issues ranged from clinical matters, to managerial practices, to statistical analysis. Clinical matters alone covered a huge range of areas on which the Inquiry needed advice, including all aspects of cardiac care and surgery, intensive care, anaesthetics, paediatric nursing, and counselling.

So as to ensure that all respectable ranges of opinion were heard in areas where disagreement was common and legitimate, the Inquiry ensured that all interested parties had a role in proposing suitable experts. Once selected, it was established as a first principle that all of the experts were the Inquiry's experts. They advised the Inquiry. They did not appear on behalf of any person or group appearing before the Inquiry. This was a crucial decision, not immediately welcomed by legal representatives. It reflected again the fact that the exercise was a Public Inquiry, in which the Inquiry decided what it wanted to hear, from whom, and in what way. It was not a court of law where 'sides' were drawn and everyone appearing was on one side or the other. In the Inquiry, there were no sides. Everyone, including (indeed, especially) experts was called by the Inquiry to assist the Inquiry.

Some of the problems posed by the Bristol Inquiry called for extremely complex research and new thinking. In at least two areas, the development of statistical tools to analyse rates of mortality and the creation of a way of reviewing a sample of case-notes, the Inquiry broke new ground. The work undertaken is still the subject of learned papers.[25]

The Inquiry also commissioned papers so as better to understand certain issues. These ranged from a history of the law and ethics relating to consent to treatment, to comparative analyses of safety in healthcare and in such industries as oil, nuclear power, railways, and aviation, to research on leadership and management. As with all other material seen by the Inquiry, they were shared with all those appearing before the Inquiry, who, on occasion, offered additional helpful comments, and, in due course, were put into the public domain.[26] Many of the papers were commissioned for Phase 2 of the Inquiry. In this Phase, the Inquiry held seven Seminars for invited experts, at which the Inquiry explored areas of importance in guiding the Inquiry towards recommendations for the future. A total of 150 participants attended and 180 papers were submitted.[27]

OPENNESS

A public inquiry works in public

Working in public was a central principle of the Inquiry: it was after all a Public Inquiry. In essence, it meant that the Inquiry made clear from the outset how it intended to work, made known the documentary and other evidence it received, held hearings in public, and made the transcripts of the hearings available to all. The purpose is obvious. I and my colleagues were carrying out a public duty. We should do so in public, so that we could properly be held to account. If the public saw the same material as did the Inquiry, the public could challenge views or conclusions, if they thought that they were not supported by the evidence. This seems to me to be an elementary principle of due process. It surprises me that it is not universally accepted.[28]

The following were some of the ways in which this principle was translated into practice.

- The Inquiry held what it called a 'Preliminary Hearing' in October, 1998 which every person and organization with an interest in the matters falling within the Inquiry's terms of reference was invited to attend. Many parents and relatives of patients treated at the BRI during the period attended. Lawyers were also present representing various groups and a wide range of organizations. The purpose of this Preliminary Hearing was to allow me as Chairman to explain the ground rules of the Inquiry: the timetable, the process for collecting evidence, and the procedure to be adopted during the hearings. One crucially important feature of the Inquiry which was made clear at this Preliminary Hearing was that there were no 'parties' appearing before the Inquiry. It was not an adversarial encounter, on the model of a trial before a court. It was an Inquiry in which the Inquiry decided what needed to be known. Those providing evidence did so with the sole purpose of assisting the Inquiry. It was not a purpose of the Inquiry (although it might be a side-effect) to hold the ring between adversaries, all intent on stating their side of the story. The Inquiry recognized no 'sides'.

- After detailed examination of the various areas of importance emerging from the evidence, and after taking the views of all those interested in the Inquiry's work, the Inquiry published what it called an 'Issues List'. As the name indicates, the list set out the issues on which the Inquiry intended to concentrate.

- After further review of all the available evidence, the Inquiry prepared a 'Core Bundle' of documents in the form of a CD. Initially, it consisted of 15,000 documents which the Inquiry regarded as central. Over time, as further evidence became available, it was added to the 'Core Bundle'. The purpose of producing the bundle was to indicate to those involved, and particularly legal representatives, the evidence that the Inquiry was particularly interested in and as regards which they could well be questioning witnesses during the hearings. The bundle was made available to legal representatives, but, since it was only intended as a procedural aid and since the documents involved would be made public as the Inquiry proceeded, it was not at that point put into the public domain.

- The date for the start of the hearings was fixed for March, 1999. This meant that six months could be spent collecting, analysing and sharing the evidence which the Inquiry was to hear and consider. Moreover, the timetable of the hearings, which occupied the following nine months, was carefully planned, so that the Inquiry could hear and consider evidence in an ordered and sequential manner, dealing with each issue in turn. It also meant that witnesses were made aware of when their evidence was required and, as regards those called to give oral evidence, when they would be called. This last point was crucial. Given that the Inquiry would wish to hear from a number of doctors and nurses still working at the Bristol Royal Infirmary, it was essential that their appearances were planned well in advance, so that the care of patients was never put at risk.

- All of the evidence seen and considered by the Inquiry was seen by all those involved in the Inquiry and was made public. Conversely, the Inquiry did not consider any evidence that was not made public.

- The Inquiry invested a considerable amount of its resources in the latest information technology (IT). The investment was one of the most important decisions taken by the Inquiry and was hugely influential throughout. The IT served a number of functions. In the context of what is being discussed here, openness and working in public, three in particular are worth mentioning. First, in the preparation for the Inquiry, every document which might serve as evidence was scanned (saved electronically) into a central system. Each document was then given a unique identifying code. Whenever it was required by the Inquiry during the hearings, it was simply displayed on large television screens which were hung from the ceiling around the Hearing Chamber (a separate set of screens showed whoever was speaking, by means of voice-activated cameras in the ceiling). Quite apart from the efficiency this brought to the proceedings, it meant that the public, which included patients, families and relatives, were able to see what the Inquiry could see. This apparently simple procedural device was of immense significance. It empowered the public by letting them in. Traditionally, in, for example, the course of a trial, documents would be pored over by lawyers, witnesses and the judge, with everyone else an onlooker of the process, but not of the document. In the Inquiry, everyone could read paragraph 3 of the letter, or whatever, at the same time as the Inquiry was reading it, and as lawyers and witnesses were offering interpretations. Not only did that further enhance accountability, but it served to make real what, to the public, would otherwise be abstract discussions. The second function served by IT was that it allowed the Inquiry to transmit the hearings to three separate locations some distance from Bristol (in Devon, Cornwall and South Wales). In this way, families and others interested in the Inquiry, were able to follow the hearings without having to travel to and stay in Bristol. Recordings of the hearings, week by week, were also kept at these locations, so that those who may have missed any were able to view them later. A third function was that, through the use of technology called 'LiveNote', which constitutes a transcript of the hearings which is transmitted instantaneously to a computer screen, the Inquiry was able to publish on its website a transcript of the day's hearings within an hour of their finishing. This particularly assisted the Inquiry in clearing up or clarifying matters which were identified from study later in the day of the day's transcript. (An additional benefit of 'LiveNote' was that lawyers could follow the hearings from their chambers and offices in real time. Not only did this save money, in that they did not have to travel to attend, but it meant that they could raise matters, by e-mail, for example, as they arose, which could then be dealt with.)

- One particular use of IT warrants separate mention. This was the creation of the Inquiry's website. It proved to be a very important source of contact and communication during the Inquiry. General information was made available, a regular Newsletter appeared, as did a series of commonly asked questions and responses to them, which were regularly updated. More formally, as part of the procedure adopted by the Inquiry, the statements of witnesses were posted, as was the Transcript of each day's hearings. By the time that the hearings ended in December 1999, the website had received over one million 'hits', and had been awarded the Department of Health's annual prize for the best website in the area of healthcare.

ACCESSIBILITY TO THE HEARINGS

Physical arrangements

While they were only a part of what the Inquiry did, the hearings were undoubtedly the most important part from the point of view of the public. It was critical, therefore, that the hearings were accessible. And here, what I am discussing is not accessibility to what went on. I have already referred to that, for example, in describing the use of IT. What is being considered here is accessibility in the sense of being able to attend, and, as important, *feeling* able to attend. Those affected by the events at the Bristol Royal Infirmary were ordinary people, not used to and perhaps inhibited by the formality and ceremony, as they might see it, which might be expected to attend a Public Inquiry. If the Inquiry was to be really accessible, very considerable thought and effort had to be put into the physical arrangements. The following are some of the more important elements of those arrangements:

Location

There were three factors which guided the Inquiry in choosing the location for the hearings. The first was that the hearings should be held in Bristol, where the hospital and staff were, and where many of the parents and others affected by the Inquiry lived or were based. Secondly, I directed the Inquiry's staff to look for a location for the hearings which was convenient in terms of transport, for those travelling within Bristol and from outside. In the event, the building chosen was close to the railway station and was easily reached by public transport. Thirdly, I directed that the building should be non-descript and functional, but should not be any sort of official or municipal building, far less a court. The reason was obvious. It was important that the public should feel comfortable and not be intimidated by their surroundings. Moreover, it was equally important that one group involved in the Inquiry, whether the Panel or the lawyers, should not feel more comfortable and more 'at home' than anyone else. On this reasoning, holding the hearings in a court or Town Hall would have been totally inappropriate. Some would have felt excluded or less confident in such surroundings. As a consequence, they might even think that the Inquiry had already 'taken sides', by holding the hearings in a place associated with authority or the exercise of power, authority and power which the families of the children who had died, in particular, felt that they were fighting. They had after all, campaigned for two or more years for a Public Inquiry to be held, with a number of disappointments along the way. To be even handed to all, and to retain the confidence of all in the integrity and impartiality of the Inquiry, attention to such apparently unimportant matters as the location of the hearings, therefore, was, in fact, of the greatest importance. Its importance lay in its symbolism as well as its utility. The location chosen was an ordinary office block. The Inquiry rented three floors, removed all internal walls and designed each floor to meet its needs.

Architects and Designers

To translate the vision of how the various floors should be configured, architects and designers were employed. One floor had to be designed to accommodate the large number of staff, including lawyers, para-legal assistants, IT specialists, researchers and administrators. These were all in one wing. In the other were the offices of members of the Panel, the Inquiry's counsel (there were 3), the Secretary to the Inquiry, and other supporting staff. On this floor there was also a secure area in which documents were stored. Another floor had to accommodate the needs of various groups representing patients and parents, plus their legal representatives to hold meetings. The principal floor housed the Hearing Chamber. There was also a meeting room for the Panel, dedicated facilities for the press and broadcast media, rooms equipped with screens to allow those who did not want to sit in the Hearing Chamber to follow proceedings, and a family room with facilities for young children.

The Hearing Chamber

Much thought was given to the design of what was, in the minds of many, the most important room, the theatre, in which the Inquiry was to be played out. I spent a number of days with architects explaining not only how the Chamber should be designed but what the principles were which informed the particular approach that I wanted. In essence, I envisaged that there should not be some central raised podium on which the Panel sat, above and, to a degree, aloof from the rest. Instead there should be a wide arc, or semi-circle, of places for the public. Facing the centre of this semi-circle, and the central focus of the room, should be the table and seat for the witnesses. After all, it was the witness who was important and whom everyone was there to hear from. Off to the left and at a tangent to the witnesses' table was the long table at which the Panel sat. Off to the right were the two tables for the Inquiry's counsel. Behind them and tucked into one side of the room were the tables for the many other counsel and solicitors who attended from time to time. Importantly, I made it clear that there should be no barrier between the front row of seats for the public, which curved around the room and went behind the Panel, and the Panel and witnesses. This created a degree of intimacy. More significantly, however, in the context of an Inquiry which attracted great anger as well as sorrow, it signified trust that the Hearings were open to all and that, in return, everyone attending would behave respectfully. This trust was never once threatened, let alone betrayed, even when the Inquiry took the evidence of those who, to some, had been responsible for their child's death. The Hearings were conducted calmly, followed attentively by audiences ranging from a handful (when some important but less interesting evidence was taken) to more than two hundred, with every seat taken. This need for an atmosphere of calm, which I thought would be crucial to the success of the Inquiry persuaded me also to spend half a day with what, in other contexts, would be called 'soft furnishings'. Given the anger, frustration and sadness of many of those who would be attending the Inquiry, I decided that one way of inducing calm was through the colours used for the carpets, the backs of chairs and other fittings. Soft, autumnal colours, such as rust and leaf green, were chosen, not just for the Hearing Chamber, but throughout the family and other rooms on that floor. It may be thought that attention to this level of detail is something of a distraction for the Chairman of a major Public Inquiry. I would profoundly disagree.

Arrangements for the Media

It must always be remembered that the media are interested in the matters which prompt a Public Inquiry and seek to write and broadcast about it. The Inquiry should assist them in this activity. To this end, dedicated facilities were made available, including a room set up for television interviews and a news-room with state-of-the-art technology. By putting these arrangements in place, the Inquiry fulfilled its responsibility to the wider audience, interested in following the progress of the Inquiry.

Witnesses

As has been said, the witnesses were the most important people in the Hearings. The Inquiry wanted to hear their stories. As important, the Inquiry wanted to give them an opportunity to have their say, to be heard, to have the sense that they had been listened to and their views understood. Some witnesses were used to the public stage. The very large majority, however, had probably never spoken in public and certainly had never been exposed to the attention which sitting at the witnesses' table attracted. If the Inquiry was to benefit from their evidence, therefore, there was a need to ensure that, as far as possible, they were not overwhelmed by their surroundings. In part, this was accomplished by briefings about the Inquiry and its procedure. But there were two specific measures taken in relation to the physical arrangements. First, every witness was given the opportunity, and most took advantage of it, to visit the Hearing Chamber in advance of giving evidence. They were given the chance to sit at the witnesses' table, get a sense of the place and have the seating arrangements explained: where the Panel were, where the Inquiry's counsel, who would be asking them questions, were and where their counsel, should they have one, would be.

Though this could not wholly remove the anxiety felt by most, it was a helpful arrangement. Secondly, the witness, if looking straight ahead, looked out at the front row of seats in the middle of the arc of public seating. That being so, this row was always reserved for members of the witness' family, supporters or friends. This meant that witnesses could always find a familiar face, should they wish to.

ACCOUNTABILITY

The Inquiry, while seeking to hold others to account for the events at the Bristol Royal Infirmary, had be accountable itself for how it conducted itself and what it did. It could not expect of others what it did not practice itself. To meet this duty of accountability, the Inquiry adopted, in particular, two practices.

Openness

As has been said, the Inquiry worked in the open. What it saw and heard by way of evidence, the public saw and heard. There can be no more simple, yet demanding, principle of accountability. The evidential basis on which any view reached by the Panel was arrived at was made explicit. In this way, any view could be challenged. As it happens, none was.

Feedback

At all stages in the Inquiry, and particularly during the Hearings, the Inquiry's staff and legal advisers sought feedback from all those affected by or involved in the Inquiry. Comments ranged from concerns about aspects of procedure, to timetabling of witnesses, to communication with various groups representing parents or patients. All comments, positive and negative were communicated to the Panel and, wherever possible acted on. It is self-evident that an essential feature of feedback is that the Panel should make it known that the comment had been received and what action, if any, had been taken (and the reason for not taking action). The Inquiry sought always to observe this principle, even to the point, on occasions, of announcing at the start of a day's hearings specific actions that had been taken. One particularly useful device was the Inquiry's website and the regular Newsletter it produced for families involved in the Inquiry.

FAIRNESS AND APPROPRIATE PROCEDURES

The Inquiry had to be even-handed and fair to all. It also had to find its way through a great mass of evidence and do so efficiently and expeditiously. To square this particular circle, the Inquiry developed an approach to working which was original in a number of respects. In large part, the originality lay in the determination of the Inquiry to hold a Public Inquiry (stressing both of those words), and not fall back on the familiar, but unsuitable, approach of a court, or of certain other Inquiries. It is fair to say that some of the proposals concerning procedure which I advanced were greeted with less than enthusiasm by advisers. But, to their credit, they were prepared to give them a fair wind and were converted. The following are, perhaps, worth noting.

Written Statements and Comments

It was important, both in terms of fairness and efficiency that the Inquiry knew what witnesses were saying, so as to decide whether they should be called to give oral evidence. It was also important that anyone referred to by a witness in any adverse manner should be made aware and have the opportunity to comment. As has already been briefly referred to, the Inquiry established a process whereby the statements of witnesses who were not to be called were made available on the Inquiry's website, together with the comment, if any, of someone identified by the Inquiry's lawyers as having been the object of criticism in the statement. The same procedure was adopted as regards witnesses who were to be called to give oral evidence, save that the statement and any comment was not put onto the Web Site until the witness had given oral evidence. The purpose of this procedure was obvious. The Inquiry would know, in advance, the contribution a particular witness would make and so could schedule the witness' appearance accordingly (given that the evidence was divided at the outset into blocks, covering different topics). Moreover, anyone referred to would have the opportunity of responding to what was said, in advance of the witness' being heard. Not only was this fair to all, but it allowed the Inquiry to take account of and explore differences of view when questioning witnesses. Moreover, it meant that the Inquiry could avoid a procedure known as the issuing of 'Salmon letters', named after Lord Justice Salmon who chaired the Royal Commission on Tribunals in 1966.[29] The purpose of 'Salmon letters' was to put individuals on notice should they have been criticised in evidence. It was a procedural response to the evidence heard, designed to ensure fairness. I took the view that it reflected an approach which equated Public Inquiries with judicial proceedings. It was, therefore, inappropriate and, moreover, unnecessary. Fairness could be maintained in a far more coherent and sensible way. In effect, the 'Salmon letters' procedure introduced an unnecessary formal step into the proceedings, which commonly provoked legal to-ing and fro-ing. By getting witnesses to reveal and confront their various accounts well in advance, everyone knew where they stood. There was no need to have resort to some additional, and time-consuming, and, frankly, out-dated procedural mechanism.

Inquisitorial rather than Adversarial

It is often said that Public Inquiries are inquisitorial by nature. But the reality often is otherwise. One explanation is that those chairing Inquiries are usually unfamiliar with how to translate the idea into practice. Moreover, since they are very commonly judges, their first instinct is to revert to what is familiar and convert the Inquiry's proceedings into a courtroom. And courtrooms, in England, are not characterized by an inquisitorial approach (with the exception of the Coroner's court). Rather they are characterized by what can be described, perhaps a little provocatively, as a gladiatorial approach. The gladiators are the lawyers, usually counsel. The judge watches and gives the thumbs up, or down, at the end. Lawyers provide a further explanation to why the proceedings, though theoretically inquisitorial, soon take on an adversarial quality. This is because lawyers also are familiar with courts and the procedure of courts. It comes as no surprise that they will seek to treat the Inquiry as if it were just another court. And their position is not just born of professional preference and comfort. It also rests on a fundamental premise, particularly of counsel, that there is only one way to discover the truth and that is through the cut and thrust of examination and cross-examination. Leave aside the fact that we have already seen that the concept of a single 'truth' may be self-delusionary, the approach misses the point of what the Inquiry is seeking to do. It is not seeking to paint a picture just in black and white; that something happened and something else did not, that someone did wrong. It does not occupy a binary world of right and wrong, good and bad. What it is trying to do is understand, and understanding rarely comes in black and white. Furthermore, whatever else may emerge from gladiatorial contest, understanding rarely does. A Public Inquiry should pursue its responsibilities in a calm and measured way, encouraging witnesses to tell their stories, and listening. It is not assisted by those who would turn it into a form of combat, in which witnesses are exposed to the forensic skill of lawyers, but something fundamental – the possibility of understanding, healing, moving on – is lost.

No 'Parties'

In keeping with its inquisitorial approach, the Inquiry made it clear that there were no 'parties', no 'sides', to advance their particular view of events. Witnesses were called by the Inquiry and were the Inquiry's witnesses. They were there to assist the Inquiry. They were not there to score points in their own favour or against others. Legal representatives initially found these challenging propositions. They were used to taking sides on behalf of a client. But, gradually, they understood.

Experts were the Inquiry's Experts

Just like other witnesses, experts also were the Inquiry's experts. They gave evidence to assist the Inquiry in its task. They did not appear so as to advance the position of this or that person or organization. They were advised as to the assistance that the Inquiry needed and gave their evidence accordingly, whether in the hearings, or in the conduct of the several analytical studies carried out by the Inquiry. Again, this was unfamiliar territory to legal representatives. They were used to experts appearing for one 'side' or another. They urged that the expert should brief them and then they would question a particular witness, or advise the Inquiry, in the light of what they gleaned from the expert's briefing. I indicated that the Inquiry wished to hear from the experts and did not wish to hear their views 'second hand', through counsel. I went further and said that the Inquiry would benefit from experts taking part in the hearings at the same time as other witnesses, so that the Inquiry could test arguments as they were put, and witnesses could refer to experts as peers, sitting alongside them, in discussing areas of technical expertise. This they did, and the Inquiry would sometimes listen spellbound as expert and witness discussed matters of significant complexity, whether it was the correct response to a particular anatomical anomaly in the heart, or why paediatric intensive care was different from the care of adults, or how a particular statistical conclusion could be arrived at. In fact, the system worked very well and counsel became advocates for it. Moreover, quite apart from giving the Inquiry the benefit of a wide range of expertise, the advice of the experts could be offered in a thoughtful and enquiring way, rather than be the product of some forensic fencing match. And, in addition, there was a wider significance in the way that the Inquiry used experts. Put simply, in their discussions in public, they made it plain how complex the issues facing the Inquiry were. They made it plain that honest professionals could legitimately differ. It was important for the public to see this, not least to dispel the notion that all that the Inquiry was dealing with was a simple story of good and bad.

Role of Counsel to the Inquiry

Counsel to the Inquiry, of whom there were three (a QC and two junior barristers), played a vital role in the Inquiry. Their first engagement was in the organization of the huge amount of material which the Inquiry collected. They prepared the 'Issues List', in consultation with the Panel, and liaised with all the other groups and organizations involved in the Inquiry. Secondly, it was their responsibility, as members of the independent Bar, to give the Inquiry legal advice. This was a continuing duty which lasted until the Inquiry published its Report. Their third, and by far their most prominent duty, was to take witnesses appearing before the Inquiry through their evidence. Because the Inquiry already had both the witness' statement and any comments from others, counsel to the Inquiry could ensure that the Inquiry heard both the witness' account, any challenges to it and their responses to these challenges. Counsel, therefore, had a role which was outside their experience. It was quite different from what they were habitually asked to do in a court. They were asked to be truly the counsel to the Inquiry, taking no sides, exploring and challenging what was said and assisting the Inquiry in any line of questioning that the Panel wished to pursue. They performed the role brilliantly.

Role of Legal Representatives

The role of counsel to the Inquiry had a significant effect on the role of those representing groups and organizations involved in the Inquiry. Prior to and after the hearings, their role was not dissimilar to that ordinarily played by lawyers. But during the hearings, it was very different. I had decided, when planning the procedure which the Inquiry should adopt, that the Inquiry would work most efficiently if its time was not taken up by each witness being subjected to questioning by the various counsel appearing before the Inquiry. The Inquiry was interested in hearing what it judged important, not what might suit the needs or interests of a particular client. The procedural mechanism adopted was to insist that questions be put by counsel to the Inquiry. The role of other legal representatives, therefore, was to relay to counsel to the Inquiry any questions or observations which they wished the witness to address. The legal representatives were not, therefore, ordinarily called upon. This saved a very considerable amount of time without impairing the Inquiry's commitment to fairness. Three exceptions to the norm that they should speak through counsel to the Inquiry were allowed by the rules drawn up. First, they could claim a short period of time at the close of a witness' evidence to clarify any uncertainties in the evidence. Initially, this right was asserted quite frequently by the various lawyers. But, over time, as they came to understand that their role was to assist the Inquiry and not to make partisan points, the legal representatives grew increasingly content to rely on counsel to the Inquiry. Indeed, it became common for legal representatives to pass notes to counsel to the Inquiry during his examination, asking for this or that point to be clarified or dealt with and this was duly done. The result was a remarkably efficient use of time. The second exception was that legal representatives could address the Inquiry before the day's hearings began, if there was some matter which had been touched on during the previous day's evidence and which, in their view, required further elaboration or comment. This was not, however, an open-ended right of address. The legal representative had to persuade counsel to the Inquiry first, and then the Inquiry, that the matter needed to be raised by addressing the Inquiry, rather than through a written submission. Given that the Inquiry dealt with large volumes of paper, this would be no great imposition, and, being part of the proceedings, I undertook that any such written submission by way of clarification would be published as part of the record of the Inquiry. In the event, this second exception was rarely exercised. The third exception was the possibility of cross-examination. I will discuss this in greater detail in the following section. Before I close this section, however, I might add that the response of the various legal representatives to this determination of their role was mixed. Some, who really wanted to turn the Inquiry into a court and put certain individuals on trial, accepted the procedure with varying degrees of reluctance. Others saw the virtue of it and responded extremely helpfully. They were helped by the extraordinary fairness and sheer hard work of counsel to the Inquiry, who left no stone unturned in their efforts to accommodate their colleagues.

Role of Cross-Examination

I have just referred to the role of cross-examination. The approach of the Inquiry warrants particular attention. It is, perhaps, helpful to notice two propositions by way of introduction. The first is that there is no *right*, as such, to cross-examination of witness (usually by lawyers) in a Public Inquiry. The Inquiry must, of course, behave fairly at all times. This does not, however, mean that cross-examination must inherently be embedded in the procedure adopted by the Inquiry in the conduct of its hearings. Fairness to all can be achieved through a variety of means. The second introductory proposition is that lawyers (especially barristers), used as they are to courtrooms, take for granted that they will be allowed to cross-examine witnesses. They tend to be convinced that only through this forensic technique, in which they are masters, can 'the truth' emerge. The position of the Inquiry was simple. It wanted to hear witnesses telling their stories, rather than have the story filtered through the interventions of their legal representatives, who might seek to gloss over this, or over-emphasise that, out of their perception of what it was good for the Inquiry to hear. It wanted to conduct the hearings with expedition. It did not want to be drawn into adversarial dogfights. And, it was convinced that proper understanding of the role of counsel to the Inquiry, and proper collaboration between them and those representing others, would mean that counsel to the Inquiry could pursue all lines of enquiry of interest to others without the need for cross-examination. This approach was not welcomed by some legal representatives. They wanted to have their 'go' at witnesses and seemed unwilling to accept that this was not the purpose of the Inquiry. Moreover, they appeared to cleave to the perhaps naïve view that 'truth' and its opposite would emerge from this particular form of jousting. The Inquiry was pressed to indicate more clearly the circumstances under which cross-examination would be allowed. A direction was duly handed down that an application, which had to be in writing, to cross-examine a witness would be considered by the Inquiry if two conditions were satisfied. The first was that the particular legal representative making the application had brought certain matters to the attention of counsel to the Inquiry as warranting exploration when a witness gave evidence. The second was that counsel to the Inquiry had failed to explore the matter, adequately or at all. In the event, no such application was ever made.[30] The Inquiry's hearings lasted for 96 days. There was not one minute of cross-examination. The impact this had on the way the Inquiry proceeded, both in terms of the expedition of its work and its atmosphere and tone, was, in my view, hugely important. Moreover, by the end of the Inquiry, it was recognized by virtually all legal representatives that the procedure had been both fair and appropriate.

The use of IT

The importance of IT to the Inquiry has already been discussed. What may be added here is its contribution to the fairness and expedition of the hearings. By scanning all relevant documents into the Inquiry's data-base, it was possible to ensure that the Inquiry, and particularly its legal team, could have access to all the relevant evidence collected at the earliest possible stage, and in a manageable form on computers. The creation of a CD containing the 'Core Bundle' achieved the same effect for both the Panel and the legal representatives of all those involved in the Inquiry. Witnesses' statements, and comments on them, were equally added to the data-base and were thus accessible to those involved. Once they began, the hearings were effectively 'paper free'. Counsel to the Inquiry, and other legal representatives on the occasions on which they addressed the Inquiry, were simply able to identify the unique code given to each document for it to be transmitted onto the computer screens of the panel, other lawyers and onto the screens available to the public. It was estimated that, by not having to search through shelves of box files to find the relevant document and the pass it around to all, but instead being able to move on at the press of a button, the Inquiry was able to accomplish anything from a quarter to a third more work on an average day of hearings.

MEETING THE NEEDS OF DIFFERENT AUDIENCES

The Inquiry had many audiences: they were in Bristol, in the South West and Wales, in Whitehall, throughout the UK and in many other countries; they consisted of patients, families of patients, doctors, nurses, managers, local and national leaders in clinical and related areas, politicians, commentators and, of course, the media. It was important for the Inquiry to recognise the differing interests and concerns of this range of audiences, and to seek to respond to them. It did so in a variety of ways, the more important of which were the following.

Patients and Families

Patients and their families reflected a spectrum of opinion about what had happened in Bristol, ranging from strong support for the surgeons and other staff responsible for the treatment of congenital heart disease during the period, to vehement and angry condemnation of them. At the beginning of the Inquiry, these groups were at loggerheads. They had different legal teams and had distinctly different hopes and expectations of the Inquiry. To ensure that the various views were heard and understood by the Inquiry, regular meetings took place between all groups and the Inquiry's staff. These meetings took place not only in Bristol, but in a number of locations in the South West and Wales. They continued up to and after the conclusion of the Inquiry and the publication of the Inquiry's Report. The Internet was also used, not only to publish documents and the transcript and to relay the hearings to other locations, but also, through its dedicated website to publish such things as regular questions and answers, the timetable for the coming months, updates on progress, and a newsletter. The aim was simple. It was to ensure that lines of communication were established and maintained, out of respect for the concerns of families and out of a desire to respond to any needs that they might have. One measure of the success of these measures, building on the extraordinary sense of fairness of the families themselves, was that, by the time that the hearings were completed, the leaders of the two principal groups of parents walked together to lay a wreath at the hospital in recognition of their common sense of loss and the understanding that the Inquiry had given them. One other measure taken by the Inquiry bears mentioning. Aware that many of the families attending or giving evidence would find the experience painful and distressing, the Inquiry took the advice of specialists in responding to the needs of grieving parents. All members of the Inquiry, from the panel, to counsel, to administrative staff, to receptionists were given intensive training. The aim was to produce an atmosphere of calm and understanding, so that anyone attending the hearings could be helped while they were there. During the hearings, the Inquiry also employed specialist counsellors who made themselves known and were available to give support and advice, if asked.

Legal Representatives

As has been explained, the Inquiry depended on the understanding and cooperation of the many legal representatives involved. This was particularly so during the early stages of the hearings, when the unfamiliar approach being adopted by the Inquiry could have created tensions. There were, therefore, very regular, often daily, meetings between counsel to the Inquiry and other lawyers and I, as Chairman, regularly responded to requests for assistance or clarification. It is right to record that, overall, the various lawyers responded with very great professionalism. Certainly, the Inquiry could not have proceeded as effectively as it did without their help.

Media

As has been made clear, the Inquiry recognized the important role of the print and broadcast media in taking the Inquiry to the wider public. The Inquiry established a dedicated team from the very beginning of the Inquiry. Their role was to assist the media. Just as in any major public event, this took many forms, from briefings, to interviews with staff (though not with the panel once the Inquiry began), to press releases, to support in explaining or clarifying this or that point. Practical arrangements were also made for the currency of the hearings, including a dedicated press room and a television studio for interviews. The difference from other public events was that the Inquiry lasted for almost three years. Thus, the team had to sustain the level of assistance, which called for stamina and patience. Also, they had to prepare for the surges of interest which happened, for example, when a particular witness appeared, culminating, of course, in the final release of the Inquiry's Report. This was a complex affair, not least to avoid leaks, and had to be choreographed against the background that, to observe the requirements of Parliamentary privilege, the Secretary of State first had to present the Report to Parliament. His statement to Parliament was transmitted to the press conference in the Queen Elizabeth II Conference Centre in central London, and the moment that he sat down, I was able to introduce the Report and respond to questions.

Government

The government of the day was interested in the Inquiry for a number of reasons. They had set it up and agreed the terms of reference. The conduct of one of the major Departments of State, the Department of Health, and a major public service, the National Health Service, were under scrutiny.

Government recognized, indeed it was explicit in the Inquiry's terms of reference, that the Inquiry would not limit itself to the circumstances of paediatric cardiac surgery in Bristol in the 80s and 90s. It would ask what the events of Bristol said about healthcare and the NHS generally and what lessons for the system as a whole could be learned. And finally, government was interested in what the Inquiry might recommend, for both good and less good (or more obviously political) reasons. That is to say, it needed to understand and be able to respond responsibly to the Inquiry's Report, and, as all governments would wish to do, to demonstrate that it was already doing (or had done!) what was recommended. The Inquiry recognized the legitimate interests of the Government in the conduct, findings and recommendations of the Inquiry. The Inquiry also recognized that the government, in the form of the Department of Health, might attract criticism for its involvement in the events of Bristol. The Inquiry, therefore, had both to liaise with Government and keep it at arms length. After all, the Inquiry was established as an *independent* Public Inquiry. Two issues needed careful attention. The first is the notion of independence. There may be some purists who think that there is a line which can be drawn, recognizable to all, which indicates what is for Government and what for the Inquiry. But, such people have little familiarity with the real world. Governments set up inquiries, they allocate funding (which comes from the taxpayer), they are interested in the efficiency of the inquiry, and are interested in, because they will be affected by, the outcome of the inquiry. It is obvious, therefore, that independence is a subtle and complex issue. It fundamentally depends on trust on both sides. Government must be confident that the inquiry will alert it to matters which are the proper concern of Government, and the inquiry must behave responsibly in this context. At the same time, Government must also have the confidence not to seek to influence or affect what the inquiry examines, how it proceeds, and what findings and recommendations it makes. In the case of the Bristol Inquiry, this trust was successfully built and sustained, notwithstanding the high public profile which the Inquiry acquired.

The second issue is one which needs to be resolved at the outset of any inquiry: whose is the report? It may be thought that the answer is obvious. An independent inquiry must necessarily produce its own report. The difficulty is that this response is question-begging. It does not answer the question; for whom is the report being produced? If the report is being produced for Government, then certain things follow. The Government may decide not to publish the report, or to publish it only in part, or in an abbreviated form. The Government may decide to publish it, but with a response or rebuttal. Clearly, any of these responses has the capacity to diminish the value of the report as an independent report. In the case of the Bristol Inquiry, I was in no doubt that the Inquiry had been asked to report to the public. The technicalities of first reporting, through the Secretary of State, to Parliament did not detract from this. Accordingly, this was established at the outset. Although there were occasions in which the Government would have wished to exercise more control over the dissemination of the Report, if not its content, the initial position prevailed.

The Report was shared with Government, as with others, under strict procedures of confidentiality. Nothing was leaked by anyone. The Government's conduct was exemplary.

Interested groups

Beyond those people and organizations immediately involved in the inquiry, there were a range of other groups who were concerned to follow the inquiry. There were professional bodies, Departments of State other than the Department of Health, NHS Health Authorities, and various other national and international organizations. To meet their needs, a dedicated liaison team was established which operated for the duration of the inquiry.

EXPLAIN WHAT THE INQUIRY IS *NOT*

Many, particularly families affected by the events at the Bristol Royal Infirmary, invested in the Inquiry a range of expectations which it could not meet. From the first days of the Inquiry, the team responsible for communications sought to make it clear what the Inquiry could and could not do, pursuant to the terms under which it was established. The message was reiterated and reinforced regularly by me during the hearings and afterwards. But, merely to say something, and to say it frequently, is not necessarily to ensure that those hearing what was said were, in fact, listening. Some saw the Inquiry as being a means of obtaining financial compensation for the wrongs that they had suffered. Others expected, or hoped, that the Inquiry would be able to impose some sort of professional disciplinary sanction on some of the clinicians. Some even wondered whether the Inquiry could impose some criminal sanction on those whom they saw as having behaved wrongly. The only answer was to keep repeating that the Inquiry was a Public Inquiry, explaining what this meant, and that it was not a court of law, nor a disciplinary tribunal. It could not award compensation nor exact disciplinary sanctions. The importance of explaining this, of explaining not only what the Inquiry was but what it was not, lay in the Inquiry's aim to meet the purposes which it was there to achieve. Catharsis, healing and learning could not be achieved unless everyone came to an understanding of what the Inquiry could and could not do. Disappointment at unrealised expectations would lead to frustration and anger. Thus, expectations had to be managed repeatedly.

MAKE A VIDEO!

In the hope that the Inquiry's approach might be of interest to others, a production company was commissioned to make a video illustrating all stages in the Inquiry, for the purposes of sharing thinking across government.

DUE SPEED?

The Inquiry took 2 years and 9 months, from the announcement by the Secretary of State to the publication of the Report. This is a significant period of time. It suggests that Governments should think long and hard before deciding that the creation of a public inquiry is the right response to a particular pressing issue. Careful thought needs to be given to whether the sort of criteria set out earlier are satisfied and whether pressure from whatever source should be resisted. That said, the period of time spent inquiring into the events in Bristol may not have been excessive, given three particular factors.

The first was the nature of the task. To review the care of over 1,800 patients over a twelve-year period, and subject it to a form of rigorous analysis not previously seen, was an immense undertaking. Secondly, it was the Bristol Inquiry which drew attention to the practice of removing and retaining the organs of patients who had died. Parents were rightly shocked. They had been unaware of the practice. The Chief Medical Officer for England, Sir Liam Donaldson, invited the Inquiry to prepare an analysis and report, not only on what had been done in Bristol, but also on the relevant ethical and legal background. This occupied over six months of the Inquiry's time in the beginning of 2000. It required the redeployment of a great many staff and, given the complexity of the issues, a great deal of the Inquiry's attention. A third factor was the judgement that, while the Inquiry should proceed expeditiously, it should not proceed at a pace faster than the capacity of those involved to understand what was unfolding. In other words, if a fundamental aim of the Inquiry was to promote understanding, this would need time.

VALUE FOR MONEY?

Did the Inquiry provide value for the money spent? This ultimately must be for others to decide. And, of course, it is not just a question of the financial outlay, but also the contribution made to meeting the various objectives that the Inquiry set for itself, particularly to promote understanding so as to contribute to learning for the future.

In financial terms, the Inquiry cost the taxpayer £14 million over the almost three years of its life. In another first for a Public Inquiry, the Inquiry published its accounts in its final Report. IT and legal representation were the two largest items of expenditure. That said, the investment in IT undoubtedly brought significant savings. Equally, the engagement of lawyers in the months leading up to the hearings, when so much preparatory work was done and much of the groundwork laid, meant that the hearings proceeded extremely smoothly and expeditiously.

The output of the Inquiry was two major reports. Beyond that, the Inquiry has had a very significant impact on the shape of policy about healthcare and the NHS.

LEARNING AND PRESCRIBING

The lessons and the prescriptions are set out in the Inquiry's reports. The Interim report was published in May, 2000. Entitled *Removal and Retention of Human Material*, it was 60 pages long, had 2 Appendices and made 69 recommendations.

The Inquiry's report was entitled, appropriately, *Learning from Bristol*. It was published in July, 2001. It was 528 pages long and had 4 appendices, which together ran to around 12,000 pages. The Report made 198 recommendations of which the Government accepted all but a handful.

POSTSCRIPT

It may be worthwhile raising one matter by way of postscript. It can be captured in the question 'What happens next?'. I raise this as a point of general constitutional importance. In general terms, once an inquiry has presented its report, it ceases to exist. It has no residuary powers. Its staff move on to new things, as do the panel and all the various experts and advisers. Given that the report has been formally presented to Parliament, the conventional procedure is that, in due course, the Government will produce its response. It may, of course, already have indicated its position, but a formal, considered response sets out the Governments position in detail.

Thereafter, it is for Parliament and interested individuals to monitor what actions, rather than words, have emerged from Government. If Government chooses not to act, which is, of course, its prerogative, there is a danger that the issues identified as warranting attention go unaddressed. One way of avoiding this inertia, would be to introduce a procedural mechanism whereby, after the publication of the report of a Public Inquiry, the Government of the day would be required to report to Parliament after six or twelve months, what action, if any, had been taken and the reasons.

NOTES

[1] The Public Inquiry into the conduct of children's heart surgery at the Bristol Royal Infirmary between 1984 and 1995.
[2] Sir Ian Kennedy KBE, FBA, LLD, DSc (Hon).
[3] As it happens, on his birthdate.
[4] 22 March 2002.
[5] See, the Select Committee's Report, *Government by Inquiry*, February, 2005.
[6] CM 5207 (1).
[7] Professor Sir Brian Jarman, Mrs Rebecca Howard and Mrs Mavis Maclean.
[8] Lord Hutton, *Report of the Inquiry into the Circumstances Surrounding the Death of Dr David Kelly*, January, 2004.
[9] Lord Butler, *Review of Intelligence on Weapons of Mass Destruction*, July, 2004.
[10] *The Inquiry into exports of defence equipment to Iraq*, 1996 (Cmnd HC 115) (Sir Richard is now Lord Scott, a Lord of Appeal in Ordinary).
[11] *The Stephen Lawrence Inquiry*, February, 1999, Cm 4262–7.

¹² *The Ladbroke Grove Rail Inquiry*, Part 1 Report. Chairman: The Rt. Hon. Lord Cullen PC HMSO 2000.

¹³ See Note 4.

¹⁴ *The Shipman Inquiry*, 1st Report Vol. 1. 'Death Disguised', HMSO 2002. Chairman: Dame Janet Smith DBE.

¹⁵ The Inquiry into BSE and Variant CJD in the United Kingdom, HMSO 2000. Chairman: Lord Phillips of Worth Matravers (appointed Lord Chief Justice of England and Wales in 2006).

¹⁶ Sir Leslie Scarman's conduct of the Brixton Inquiry (*Scarman Inquiry into the Brixton Riots*, 1982) is often cited in rebuttal. In my view, it merely serves as the exception to the rule. It is interesting to note that the Inquiries Act, 2005, seeks to occupy a middle ground. While not stating that judges should not be appointed as Chairs, Ministers are required, by section 10, to consult, in the case of England, the senior Lord of Appeal in Ordinary or the Lord Chief Justice, if they propose to appoint a sitting judge as chair, or even a member of the panel, of an Inquiry.

¹⁷ I do not, in this paper, describe the content of the Inquiry's Report and Recommendations, but they did amount to a systematic analysis of, and blueprint for, all aspects of healthcare.

¹⁸ See, for example, *The Allitt Inquiry*, Department of Health, 1994.

¹⁹ The Commission was established under the Health Act, 1999 and abolished in 2004, when the Commission for Healthcare Audit and Inspection (known as the Healthcare Commission) came into being, by virtue of the Health and Social Care Act, 2003.

²⁰ Professor Emeritus of Psychology, University of Manchester is a world-renowned expert on human error and 'human factors' theory.

²¹ The doctors were the two surgeons carrying out paediatric cardiac surgery and the chief executive of the hospital trust.

²² One of the several odd features of the Inquiry under Sir Richard Scott (see note 10) was that he made no recommendations.

²³ The recently enacted Inquiries Act, 2005, goes some way to fill the gap I refer to, but the provisions of the Act are couched in very general terms. They still leave a great deal to the discretion of the Chair, e.g., section 17(1) provides: '… the procedure and conduct of an inquiry are to be such as the chairman of the inquiry may direct.'

²⁴ See Appendix 3 of the Report (note 1) for a complete list of those who gave evidence, whether orally or in writing, to the Inquiry.

²⁵ See e.g. Spiegelhalter, D.J., Kinsman, R., Grigg, O., and Treasure, T., (2003) 'Risk-adjusted sequential probability ratio tests; applications to Bristol, Shipman, and adult cardiac surgery', *International Journal of Quality in Healthcare* 15, 7–13.

²⁶ See Annex B of the Report (note 1).

²⁷ Ibid.

²⁸ But compare the views expressed by Lord Justice Simon Brown in *R v SoS for EFRA, ex p Persey* [2003], and the deeply equivocal provisions in section 19 of the Inquiries Act, 2005. Of course, most of the circumstances contemplated as warranting privacy, even in a Public Inquiry, involve matters which I would categorize as falling into Type A (ante) and thus not matters properly for a Public Inquiry.

²⁹ Cmnd 3121 (1966).

³⁰ A request was made to recall a witness, when the Inquiry revealed the extent to which tissue had been removed from children who had died. The request was denied. Recalling the witness would not have added to the Inquiry's understanding, although it would have allowed some the opportunity to pursue further an issue which engendered very strong emotions.

ETHICS AND INFERTILITY

**The third lecture in the series, delivered on
11th February 2003 by Baroness Deech of Cumnor DBE, MA**

ABSTRACT

The birth of Louise Brown, the first IVF baby, led to consideration of the ethical factors inherent in the separation of artificial and natural reproduction. The Warnock Report recommendations are central to the Human Fertilisation and Embryology Act 1990 and the work carried out under that Act by the regulatory body created, the Human Fertilisation and Embryology Authority. Recent developments, such as cloning and stem cell research, preimplantation genetic diagnosis and sex selection, continually produce new ethical dilemmas that the HFEA must consider and resolve. Within a legal framework comprising the Act, human rights and European legislation, it has evolved five ethical principles to guide it in monitoring and regulating embryo uses: (i) the assurance of human dignity, worth and autonomy. Nobody should be treated as a convenience or bank of spare parts; (ii) the welfare of the potential child; (iii) safety first – the birth of healthy babies must be the aim, not risk or experiment; (iv) respect for the embryo and human life at all stages; and (v) the saving of life. Various well known legal cases are discussed, for example, the *Blood* case, and recent attempts to save the life of one child by giving birth to another with matching tissue. There is particular Jewish interest in creating a healthy family and an emphasis on life and pragmatism. Lord Jakobovits was a leading and early exponent of the new ethical dilemmas in this field.

Ethical considerations are central to the Human Fertilisation and Embryology Act 1990 and the work carried out under the Act by the regulatory body created, the Human Fertilisation and Embryology Authority (HFEA). New developments in science, for example cloning, continually produce new ethical dilemmas that the HFEA must consider and resolve. Recent legislation and political developments have created further frameworks within which we must work, and are not always consistent with each other. Examples are the Human Rights Act, 1998, recent European

Conventions on Biomedicine and allied matters and the development of certain provisions in the European Treaty, in particular, the guaranteed freedom of movement to seek medical services and freedom of movement of goods.

A fundamental balancing act was performed when it was decided in the UK that embryo use and research should be regulated by law. Answers had to be found to some searching questions. How was the humane treatment of infertile couples and the research appended to it, together with public fear and distrust, to be managed? How was the omnipotent facet of the clinicians (one of whom has been heard to say: 'I have made a thousand women pregnant') to be balanced against the vision of the feared alchemist? How are individuals to be given the maximum appropriate access to new technology while refraining from causing a woman or man to feel labelled as inferior or unfulfilled because they were childless? How was efficient treatment of a woman, especially an older one, to be managed, given the risk of multiple births with all their attendant dangers if too many embryos were replaced in one cycle? The Warnock Report of 1984 attempted to address many of these questions. The Report remains to this day unrivalled in its depth and pragmatism and has provided a stimulus to other countries to tackle the problem of regulation and legislation in similar fashion.

Further opportunities now exist to understand more about the process of early human development, the causes of genetic disease, of miscarriage and infertility, and many other serious health challenges. The most recent developments in stem cell research may offer a more effective treatment to individuals and couples who suffer these problems. Yet there are those in society who believe that IVF is fundamentally wrong in breaching the essential link between sexual intercourse in marriage and reproduction. For those who believe that each individual life begins at the moment of conception, IVF is fundamentally wrong, and embryo research and the use or wastage of surplus embryos are wholly immoral (see the argument advanced by the appellant Quintavalle on behalf of the Pro-Life Alliance in *R v Secretary of State for Health ex parte Quintavalle* [2003] UK HL concerning cell nuclear replacement and the regulatory scope of the Human Fertilization and Embryology Act 1990).

Assisted reproduction poses particular ethical dilemmas. Where, for example, should the balance be struck between guarding a couple's privacy and ensuring the welfare of any potential child? This problem manifests itself in two ways. First, there is a need for follow-up studies of children born by IVF techniques, none of whom is older than 25 at the moment. There are suggestions of a higher abnormality rate. Nevertheless, as with adoption, there is an equally compelling argument that a family raising a child is entitled to privacy and it must be accepted that they may not even tell the child of its origins, thus blocking the essential research. Second, the HFEA Code of Practice (5th edn) requires clinics to: 'seek to satisfy themselves that the general practitioner of each prospective parent knows of no reason why either of them might not be suitable for the treatment of be offered. This would include anything that might adversely affect the welfare of any resulting child.'[1] However, increasing numbers of general practitioners will not answer enquiries from clinics, either because of fear of breach of confidentiality, or because they feel that they cannot judge any person's fitness to be a parent, given that nature would not have done so if she had been able to take her course. Another well-known dilemma is the treatment of HIV patients who wish to be parents. Are society's fears and concerns sufficient reason to place limits on scientific and clinical developments?

IVF treatment has come a long way in a relatively short space of time. It is no longer regarded by many people within the medical profession as particularly novel and worldwide there are probably one million IVF children, 50,000 in the UK. But it should not be forgotten that a few years ago it was a novel and, for many people, a rather frightening technique. Louise Brown, the first UK IVF baby is 25. She said in an interview on her 18th birthday: 'I'm just an ordinary girl. All I am thinking about at the moment is becoming a nursery nurse.' Her IVF younger sister already has two babies of her own, naturally conceived.

So have assisted reproduction techniques become ordinary? Or is there still a need to keep examining them to ensure that they do not offend society's codes of acceptability? It is proposed here that they do still need to be examined. New techniques and new opportunities appear regularly; new problems emerge. Development should not necessarily be halted or even necessarily slowed down, but one should ensure that public understanding, acceptance and reassurance move at the same pace.

The legislation provides a framework that translates ethical considerations into practical applications. The following principles that have been developed and applied are derived partly from the statute and partly from practice:

1 The assurance of human dignity, worth and autonomy. Hence, nobody should be treated as a convenience or a bank of spare parts. Consent and counselling are vital.
2 The welfare of the potential child. Consideration of its need for a father is enshrined in the Act[2] – hence, the concern about cloning and the difficult family relationships it would cause. The HFEA banned embryo splitting in 1993 and in 2001 the government moved rapidly to close any possible loophole by enacting the Human Reproductive Cloning Act 2001.
3 Safety first. The birth of healthy babies must be the aim, not risk or experiment. Hence consideration of the high risks attaching to multiple births, such as low birth weight, cerebral palsy, early deaths, and stress on the family, has led to the requirement that only two embryos be replaced in any given treatment cycle. This is sometimes resented by clinicians but is a rule designed in support of public health and welfare.
4 Respect for the embryo and human life at all stages dominates our law and its application. The embryo is given a special status by the legislation. The free and informed choice of each patient is expressed in their consent, which may be withdrawn. There is concern for the welfare and individuality of the potential child, and his or her legal, social and genetic parenthood with its attendant privileges and duties.

Contributions to the ethical debates are also being made increasingly by international treaties. For example, in 1997 UNESCO published a Universal Declaration on the Human Genome and Human Rights. Article 11 of this says: 'practices which are contrary to human dignity, such as reproductive cloning of human beings, shall not be permitted.' This is echoed in the European Parliament Resolution on Cloning passed on 13th March 1997. These two instruments refer to reproductive cloning, that is the cloning intended to lead to a baby, which is distinct from therapeutic cloning, that is the creation of an embryo the purpose of research and its maintenance only for that purpose.

A number of cases and situations may serve to illustrate the operation of the ethical principles and treaties referred to above.

THE BLOOD CASE

Mrs Blood's second child was born recently some seven years after the death of her husband from meningitis. While much has been written about the European law aspects of the case[3] very little has been said, despite the HFEA's best efforts, on the topic that seemed to the HFEA to lie at the heart of the case. This was the ethics and legality of removing sperm from dying and unconscious men. In the wake of the publicity surrounding the Blood case, the HFEA staff received many telephone calls at all times of the day and night seeking advice or permission to remove sperm from dying men, usually after traffic accidents. All callers were told that this was and remains illegal without prior consent. It seemed to the HFEA that the Court of Appeal's judgment did not deal with the basic issue of consent on the facts of the case, namely, whether it should be legal for gametes to be removed from the many thousands of young people who die unexpectedly every year from accident or illness leaving behind a bereft widow or widower, fiancé or fiancée, parents, grandparents or partners. The practical difficulties of having to decide, in the few hours available for the procedure to be carried out effectively, whether the person calling for the removal of the gametes is entitled to do so, and what category of person that should extend to, and whether the same consideration should apply to the removal of eggs or ovaries from a dying woman, and whether she should be kept alive on a ventilator in order to give birth, or whether her eggs should be fertilized and stored, and for how long storage should continue, are major, and fraught with the greatest ethical issues imaginable.

These issues were debated in Parliament[4] and subsequently the government established a review of the law of written consent in medical treatment.[5] The report concluded that the law of written consent was a good one and should not be changed and that the HFEA should expressly be told not to allow export of sperm to overcome breaches of British law. The HFEA has always maintained that the ethical issue in the Blood case was the need to preserve human autonomy by insisting on written consent; also, even more strongly, one should prevent the unwarranted assault on the unconscious and dying that would inevitably precede the removal of sperm without consent in the emergency situation typified by the facts in the Blood case. Regrettably, the procuring of the sperm did not feature largely in the legal arguments.

The Council of Europe Convention on Human Rights and Biomedicine of 1997, Article 8, reverts to this situation: 'when because of an emergency situation the appropriate consent cannot be obtained, any medically necessary intervention may be carried out immediately for the benefit of the health of the individual concerned.' The removal of sperm at the request of another is not an intervention for the benefit of the health of the dying person, nor is it medically necessary. Otherwise, all common law and European principles insist on informed consent.

Arguably in the Blood case the way in which the gametes were removed from the dying husband would have enabled the HFEA validly to continue to refuse permission to export them on the ground that the treatment sought was based on something seriously contrary to the ethical rules prevailing in Britain.[6] Thus the transaction was illegal or immoral as a matter of British law and policy and perhaps should not have been allowed to be regarded as a 'service' in European law. It is unlikely, although not established, that any member state of the EC allows gametes to be removed from the dying and unconscious without their consent and knowledge; some indeed ban posthumous insemination. Had money and pressures at the time been more relaxed, the HFEA would have been able to establish that there was a public interest to be protected in the Blood case which justified an infringement of the European right of provision of services. The public interest consisted in protection of the body, human autonomy, the protection of human dignity and freedom of choice, respect for reproductive tissues, and respect for the family of two living parents.

The HFEA was, and remains, concerned with the human rights of an unconscious or dying patient. It should be noted that the existing laws of consent are wide enough to permit cancer patients routinely to put sperm into storage before undergoing potentially sterilizing treatment. It is also the case that child law enables parents to consent to the removal of testicular tissue from a small child facing damaging radiotherapy treatment for cancer. If advances in science continue and the child, hopefully, survives to maturity, he will have the opportunity to consent to reimplantation and fertility treatment.

The Blood judgment should be compared with *St George's Health Care NHS Trust v S*.[7] Here it was held that even the unreasonable desire of a competent patient to refuse a caesarean must be respected. It was held that if the pregnant mother were incapable of consent, her best interests should be considered and that in cases of doubt as to competency, the question should be referred to the Court. This all applies where the patient's health or life is at risk. How much more so, then, should the body of a dying patient, whose interests cannot be served in any way, be respected and not desecrated by the removal of gametes without his or her knowledge.

THE ASSISTED REPRODUCTION AND GYNAECOLOGY CENTRE CASE 2002

In the Court of Appeal the HFEA recently succeeded in preventing an unacceptable practice. The Medical Director of the Assisted Reproduction and Gynaecology Centre, Mr Mohamed Taranissi, had an infertile patient, Mrs H. He and his patient challenged a ruling by the HFEA given at the appellants' request. At the material time, the HFEA Code of Practice stated that 'no more than three eggs or embryos should be placed in the woman in one cycle, regardless of the procedure used'. Mr. Taranissi wished to treat Mrs H by using five embryos and argued that it was appropriate to make an exception to the rule in Mrs H's case, based on her particular treatment needs. Mrs H was 47. She married when she was 41. She and her husband were unable to conceive a child. In May 1996, she consulted Mr Taranissi. Between June 1996 and July 2000, Mrs H underwent eight IVF treatment cycles, in each of which three of her embryos were replaced in the uterus. Mrs H did not, however, become pregnant. Mr Taranissi subsequently wrote to the HFEA inviting it to consider a relaxation on the ban on the insertion of more than three embryos in relation to older patients. He claimed that the risk of any such woman having a multiple birth was non-existent but that the use of more than three embryos might give her a reasonable chance of conceiving. The Authority carefully considered such statistics as there were relating to pregnancies and multiple births among women of that age, both in this country and abroad. It found that the birth rate was very low indeed but that, where pregnancy did occur there was some risk of a multiple birth, all the more threatening at an older age. It therefore advised Mr Taranissi to uphold the rule of the Code of Practice and was not willing to allow a relaxation as an exceptional case.

The appellants sought judicial review. The Authority in its reasoning made it clear that it wished to minimize as far as possible the health risks arising from multiple pregnancies and multiple births, including the risk to any child that is born and is damaged by obstetric or neonatal complications. The HFEA pointed out that multiple pregnancies can lead to a much higher risk of complications during pregnancy, premature birth and low birth rate, disability and neonatal death. Low birth weight babies, it pointed out, are much more likely to suffer from serious lifelong health problems such as cerebral palsy. The cost of these problems also places a financial burden on the NHS and society (it should be noted that 80% of the IVF work in Britain is private and expensive, but subsequent pregnancies and complications are carried by the NHS). The HFEA considered carefully whether in this case the transfer of more than three embryos would be likely to significantly enhance the chance of Mrs H becoming pregnant, and whether any such benefit was outweighed by a greater risk of a multiple pregnancy. The Authority assessed both the general state of clinical knowledge and the available statistics and the facts of this case. Although selective foetal reduction of multiple pregnancies is sometimes practised, the Authority, respectful towards embryos, is anxious to avoid multiple pregnancies, not just births.

The HFEA advised that it had approached the case of Mrs H on the basis that Articles 8 and 12 of the European Convention on Human Rights and Fundamental Freedoms might apply. It expressed the opinion that any interference with those rights was in accordance with the law, given that the HFE Act required it to determine what constitutes suitable practice and to give appropriate advice. The HFEA also specifically considered whether the interference pursued a legitimate aim and decided that it did – namely the obviation of the health risks and costs of multiple pregnancy and multiple births. Finally, in considering proportionality, the HFEA balanced the importance of the need for interference against any detriment to the rights of the individual patient, Mrs H. The HFEA did not consider that the interference with the rights in this particular case was more than necessary to meet the legitimate aim.

Sedley LJ found that the human rights claim had been based throughout on an unargued assumption that Article 8 and Article 12 rights were engaged. He saw no reason to assume that they were. But if they were, they had been contingently addressed with care by the HFEA. In the Court of Appeal Mr Justice Wall[8] found that the Authority's reasoning could not be described as irrational. He observed that this was an area of rapidly developing science in which judicial review had a limited role to play. Disagreements between doctors and scientific bodies in this pioneering field were inevitable. The UK, through the HFE Act, had opted for a system of licensing and regulation. The HFEA was the body empowered by Parliament to regulate. Like any public authority, it is open to challenge by way of judicial review, if it exceeds or abuses the powers and responsibilities given to it by Parliament: but where, as was manifest in this case, it considered requests for advice carefully and thoroughly, and produced opinions which were plainly rational, the court, in his judgment had no part to play in the debate and certainly no power to intervene to strike down any such decision. The fact that the appellants may disagree with the HFEA's advice was neither here nor there.

Albeit a decision on the limits of judicial review, this was a useful one in upholding the ethical principles espoused by the HFEA of safety, welfare of the child and respect for the embryo.

THE HASHMI CASE 2002

The media have extensively canvassed the case of the Hashmi family. They have a child, Zain, who suffers from the unpleasant and life-threatening disease of Beta-Thalassaemia. His prognosis is not good and daily invasive treatment is necessary. The Hashmis were informed of the need for a donor or stem cells whose tissue would match that of the affected child. They conceived another child naturally in the hope that the new baby's umbilical cord blood would help to cure Zain, but the new baby was not a match for him. Unwilling to continue to conceive children who might not only suffer from the same disease Beta-Thalassaemia, but who also would not match the needs of the affected child, they applied through a clinic to the HFEA for a licence for a novel procedure. They wished first of all for preimplantation genetic diagnosis: this is a procedure which is allowed by the HFEA only in serious cases of life-threatening inherited disease. It enables parents to select an embryo, created by IVF, which is shown by biopsy after a few days of development to be free of the feared disease. This procedure has only been used in limited cases surrounded by strict regulation and licence. The public was consulted about preimplantation genetic diagnosis and their responses supported the HFEA approach. So far, this would be a straightforward request. But the Hashmis also wished to narrow the selection of an embryo to choose one that, if Mrs Hashmi were to become pregnant, would result in a baby whose blood would be compatible with that of Zain. It should be noted that there was only a 1 in 16 chance of selecting such an embryo and that a pregnancy consequent on this procedure would have a very slim chance indeed of succeeding. Statistically, the odds were against the Hashmis. Nevertheless a decision in principle had to be made. It has become unfortunately known as 'designer baby' but could also be said to be the choice of a healthy child for a life saving reason.

The HFEA considered the request carefully over a number of months. It noted that s.13(5) of the HFE Act contained a provision relating to the welfare of any child that may be born as a result of treatment services: 'a woman shall not be provided with treatment services unless account has been taken of the welfare of any child who may be born as a result of the treatment (including the need of that child for a father), and of any other child who may be affected by the birth.' This is interpreted further in Part III of the Fifth Edition of the HFEA Code of Practice 'in deciding whether or not to offer treatment, centres should take account both of the wishes and needs of the people seeking treatment and of the needs of any children that may be involved. Neither consideration is paramount over the others, and the subject should be approached with great care and sensitivity.' The HFEA also considered Article 8 of the UK Human Rights Act 1998, that is the right to respect for private and family life. It also considered Article 12 (the right to marry and found a family) and Article 14, the prohibition of discrimination. The HFEA then asked itself whether PGD with HLA typing (the match required in the Hashmi case) was compatible with the welfare of the unborn child, compatible with the public good and whether morally significant criteria could be found to demarcate acceptable and unacceptable reasons for the conception and selection of embryos.

The HFEA reminded itself that there was a presumption in law that people should be free to exercise their rights in areas of activity that most closely affect themselves and their families. A public authority should only interfere with the exercise of these rights in the interests of public health or morals. Where it does interfere, this interference must be proportionate and the presumption for intervening should be strong. Given that the choice to select an embryo with certain characteristics is technically available, the case of the Hashmis could be posed in terms of whether it would be morally justifiable for the state to withhold this choice as a matter of public policy. However, it was a matter of concern that to approach this question from a perspective of the rights of parents led uncomfortably to issues of eugenics. This should therefore be balanced by a proportionate public policy response. In looking at the ethical background, the HFEA considered parental motivation. It could be suggested that positive consideration of the welfare of the child requires respect for beings as ends and that the putative child be treated not simply as a means to a further end but also always as an end in itself.[9] The parents' motivation is an important factor in considering the welfare of the child and it is usually expressed as the parents wanting the child for its own sake and not simply to fulfil some further end they have in mind. It may be impossible, however, to discover the parents' motivation by empirical interrogation. To enquire into motivation for having children is a very modern issue. From the beginning of mankind until the end of the 20th century, a child would arrive or not arrive, to work for the family or to be raised as the parents wished and the issue of why or whether they should do this could not be raised. Even in these days of choice, it is not incompatible with the welfare of the child that the parents' desire for the child for its own sake is not their primary or sole motivation. In its guidance as to the welfare of the child the HFEA imposes high standards and expectations with regard to prospective parents. It is also noted that there are many common reasons why children are conceived naturally which would not satisfy the welfare of the child assessment. Benefit and harm in the case were also balanced. On the one hand, the parents might choose not to have a child at all and then the child would never exist. On the other, the child's birth could be identified with the welfare of the family, that is the welfare of Zain, which is expressly referred to in the HFE Act. It was suggested that this could be interpreted positively, that is, improving the welfare, as well as negatively, that is, not decreasing his welfare.

The HFEA also considered the public good. It was suggested that the selection of embryos for particular genetic characteristics was the thin end of the wedge and that there was slippery slope from this to eugenic breeding. This would not be for the public good. On the other hand, it could be argued that there was the possibility of choosing a morally significant factor that could be identified to demarcate those uses of the PGD technique that were acceptable and those that were not. It was thought that such a line could be drawn. Non-serious or treatable conditions would not justify such embryo selection. Nor would the HFEA ever permit the selection of an embryo to act as a tissue donor for a parent but only for a sibling. Selecting an embryo for some non-medical reason would also have to be carefully guarded. Genetically modifying an embryo is explicitly prohibited in the HFE Act.[10] An alternative to embryo selection in this case would be prenatal selection. That is, the selective abortion of naturally conceived foetuses that were shown by prenatal diagnosis to be affected or not an appropriate tissue match. The cost in terms of the abortion of otherwise viable foetuses, the physical and psychological harm to the woman and the family, and the delay to the treatment of the suffering sibling, are likely to be significant, but it is known that some families are prepared to follow this route. In the end the HFEA agreed that the PGD with HLA typing could be compatible with the welfare of the unborn child. Any family proposing to go to such lengths is likely to possess extraordinary strength by virtue of having reached this decision, even though the family context is likely to be highly stressful. Not much weight was placed on motivation since it is clear that the family's motivation for having a child naturally cannot reliably be discovered. For the element of utility in the parents' decision to conceive for a particular purpose does not rule out their benevolent intention to love and care for the child. The HFEA felt that tissue donation was not in itself a problematic reason for having children and was certainly no worse than other common reasons. Once the child was born, it would have its full human rights and were there ever to be any question of further invasive treatment of the child; it would have to be made a ward of court, as would any naturally conceived child in those circumstances. The only treatment envisaged here was the use of umbilical cord blood, which would otherwise be thrown away. Bone marrow donation, as explained above, comes into a different category. This represented a safe scientific technique that could be used benevolently and there seems to be no reason to stop it.

Nor could it reasonably be described as eugenics, because the explicit purpose of the treatment is to cure a particular existing condition, nor to eradicate the condition from the gene pool entirely. The HFEA ruled that all other possibilities for treatment and existing sources of tissue for the affected child should have been explored before PGD with HLA typing should be allowed. The condition of the affected child should be severe or life-threatening, of a degree of seriousness that would support the use of PGD irrespective of considerations relating to tissue donation. The demand to be made on the new baby should be restricted to cord blood and the harvesting of other organs would be unacceptable and, indeed, illegal without court consent. Embryos may not be genetically modified in order to provide a tissue match. It remains to be seen whether the Hashmis' proposed procedures will succeed. Thus there has emerged a new ethical principle in fertility treatment: the use of the techniques to save life. Comment on Reproductive Ethics (CORE – one of the Pro-Life Alliance groups) applied for judicial review of the HFEA's Hashmi decision, and succeeded at first instance.[11] However, CORE lost on appeal in May 2003 and also in the House of Lords in March 2005.[12]

These are illustrations of the application of the ethical principles. They are not easy but they are intensely rewarding. It was a privilege to serve on a committee entrusted with decisions that go to the heart of our perceptions of our identity and our existence as individuals. It should be noted that by law half the committee are lay persons and may not be connected with the profession of assisted reproduction. In particular, the Chairman and Deputy Chairman must be lay persons. More than half the committee are women. Appointments are made following Nolan principles after advertisement. The HFEA is accountable to the Minister for Public Health and places an Annual Report before parliament. It is therefore reasonably confident in its accountability and transparency. The HFE Act has stood the test of time and is flexible and delegatory in its structure. There is a great deal of interest in it abroad and a number of countries, including Australia, Canada, Japan and Germany, are considering similar models for themselves.

NOTES

[1] Para 3.20.

[2] Section 13 (5).

[3] *R v HFEA ex p Blood* [1997] 2 All ER 627.

[4] *Lords Hansard*, 5 Dec. 1996 col., 802 et seq; *Commons Hansard* 30 Oct 1996 col. 596 et seq.

[5] Professor Sheila McLean, *Review of the Common Law Provisions relating to the removal of gametes and of the consent provisions in the Human Fertilisation and Embryology Act 1990 (July 1998)*

[6] Hervey (1998), 'Buy, Baby: The European Union and Regulation of Human Reproduction', (1998) *Oxford Journal of Legal Studies* 18, 207.

[7] [1998] 3 WLR 936.

[8] [2002] EWCA CIV 20.

[9] Immanuel Kant's Categorical Imperative.

[10] Schedule 2, paragraph 1(4) prohibits the genetic modification of any cell while it forms part of an embryo.

[11] Case No. CO/1162/02.

[12] *Quintavalle v Human Fertilisation and Embryology Authority* [2005] UKHL 28 on appeal from [2003] EWCA CIV 667.

RESPECT: AN ESSENTIAL PART OF QUALITY HEALTHCARE

The fourth Lord Jakobovits Commemorative Lecture, delivered on 10th February 2004 by Professor Sir Liam Donaldson MSc, MD, FRCS(Ed), FFPHM, FRCP, FRCP, (Ed)

ABSTRACT

Rabbi Lord Immanuel Jakobovits made major contributions to Jewish Medical Ethics, many of which have universal application. People are now much more aware that healthcare has an ethical dimension and wish to contribute to the resolution of ethical dilemmas. A number of topics illustrate this public involvement, with stem cell research just one example: the UK law, following much public and Parliamentary debate, now allows for stem cell research under strict controls and conditions. In daily life, a fundamental ethical principle in the delivery of healthcare is respect for the individual patient: this applies both in relating to individuals and in setting up systems to provide and assure good, safe care.

The need for explicit standards of care has become more prominent with the recognition that 'bad' doctors exist. The accountability of doctors and other health professionals has become more tangible with increased formality in the management of the NHS. The General Medical Council has produced explicit criteria for the ethical practice of health care, and the application of evidence-based medicine is regarded as of the utmost importance to avoid significant delays in the uptake of effective treatments and also the substantial variations that exist in clinical decision-making and practice across the NHS. The media has brought a number of 'medical scandals' to the public's attention. Investigation of 'problem doctors' has often revealed difficulties with systems, such as the failure of colleagues (for whatever reason) to act against a fellow professional. Patients' rights have also gained prominence.

The problems at Alder Hey Children's Hospital highlighted the wide gulf between the views of parents and prevailing opinion within the medical profession over organ retention. These concerns led to the introduction of the Human Tissue Bill (as the Human Tissue Act 2004) to govern the taking, storage and use of human organs and tissues. Individual rights are assured, yet the needs of research, education, training and public health are also catered for.

In the 1990s, a radical programme of clinical governance was introduced to systematically improve standards of care and protect patients in the NHS. Every health care organisation has introduced quality assurance and quality improvement programmes. Mechanisms are now in place for early identification, analysis and learning to take place when lapses in patient care occur. Increasingly, failures are dealt with openly and constructively, not simply by punishment.

The Government established the National Patient Safety Agency in 2001, which encourages the reporting of the safety breaches and 'near misses', that are thought to occur in as many as 1 in 10 hospital admissions. As in other walks of life, failures in health care are most often due to a series of individual, organisational and management weaknesses as well as to technological and socio-cultural problems. By the end of 2003, nearly 600 independent Patient and Public Forums (involving over 4000 people) gave feedback about healthcare services. An Independent Complaints Advocacy Service (ICAS) has been set up and patients can also obtain help from the Patient Advice and Liaisons Service operated by NHS Trusts. The General Medical Council has undergone significant reform over the last few years and a process of revalidation is under development.

The balance of power between health professionals and patients has shifted in favour of the patient. Moving on from the paternalistic pattern of the past, respect for the patient is now centre-stage, influencing the shape of organisations, defining the professional standards and values that are found throughout the health system.

Sir Liam Donaldson, England's Chief Medical Officer, celebrates the fundamental messages of Rabbi Lord Jakobovits and stresses the importance of respecting patients in the process of reforming health systems.

One of the most important contributions of Rabbi Lord Immanuel Jakobovits (1921–99) was the application of classical Jewish thought on medical ethics to problems of the day.

His first landmark publication *Jewish Medical Ethics*, released in 1959, illuminated the wisdom of historical pronouncements for a wide audience. Prior to that time, extensive guidance from Jewish leaders on medical practice was inaccessible to many modern readers.

This publication, which is now considered a classic, simultaneously reflected the diversity of Jewish views on medical ethics and the possibility for universal application of some historical religious edicts. It also documented early thought about subjects that continue to stir important ethical questions today, such as abortion, artificial insemination, autopsy and euthanasia. This piece of work and subsequent influential publications would ultimately establish Jakobovits' reputation as the 'grandfather of modern Jewish medical ethics'.[1]

Fig. 1

Ten basic Jewish principles affecting medical care were described by Rabbi Lord Jakobovits as the following:

- Human life is sacrosanct, and of supreme and infinite worth.
- Any chance to save life, however remote, must be pursued at all costs.
- The obligation to save a person from any hazard to his life or health devolves on anyone able to do so.
- Every life is equally valuable and inviolable, including that of criminals and prisoners.
- One must not sacrifice one life to save another, or even any number of others.
- No one has the right to volunteer his life.
- No one has the right to injure his own or anyone else's body, except for therapeutic purposes.
- No one has the right to refuse medical treatment considered necessary by competent opinion.
- Measures involving some immediate risks of life may be taken in attempts to prevent certain death later.
- There is no restriction on animal experiments for medical purposes.

When ethical dilemmas arise, a natural response is to seek answers from moral leaders of past and present.

This holds true in the field of medicine, where practitioners face life and death decisions every day, just as it does in any other sphere of life.

Rabbi Jakobovits was born in Koenigsberg, Germany. In 1936, he fled Nazism and moved to Britain, where he completed religious studies and then assumed position as Rabbi of the Great Synagogue in London.

In later years, he became Chief Rabbi of Great Britain and the Commonwealth. He was the first chief rabbi to be knighted and the first to be appointed to the House of Lords.

In the course of his career he was often called upon to comment on challenging moral issues. At one point, in response to concerns about the ethics of clinical research, he outlined ten basic Jewish principles that could be applied to questions about human experimentation (see figure 1 above).[2]

Some of these principles have universal application and are worth remembering for all those interested in the ethics of medical care. For example, there was a recognition that human life is sacrosanct and of supreme, infinite worth. Furthermore, every life was deemed to be equally valuable and inviolable.

ETHICS AND PUBLIC DISCOURSE

At the start of the 21st century, most people are aware that healthcare has an ethical dimension and increasingly they want the opportunity to contribute to the resolution of ethical dilemmas.

The shift away from ethics as a purely professional concern to a public issue that requires broad consideration and participation represents a significant change in recent years.

From the specialist professional point of view, the field of ethics has always been broad. But in the public sphere, it has mainly been associated with certain big topics, notably euthanasia, abortion and confidentiality.

Stem cell research is an example of a new topic that has a major ethical dimension and has been debated in the public arena from the beginning. Unlike the United States, the UK has legislation allowing the use of embryonic cells for research purposes under strict controls.

Stem cells have the potential to develop into almost any tissue of the body and so could enable the treatment of diseases currently classified as incurable, such as paraplegia, Parkinson's Disease and some forms of cancer. For this reason, the majority of people in the UK support stem cell research. But a significant minority believes that the use of any embryo for research purposes is unethical and unacceptable on the grounds that an embryo is a human being entitled to full human status from the moment of conception. Pro-life advocates and some religious groups argue that such research should be banned.

The UK government's position is that research is warranted across a range of sources of stem cells – including embryos created by in vitro fertilisation or cell nuclear replacement – because it holds great potential to relieve suffering and treat disease. Embryo research is therefore permitted under strict controls and conditions.

The UK law reflects nearly twenty years of public and Parliamentary debate. Whilst protection of the embryo is deemed important, successive governments have supported efforts to pursue all areas of stem cell research responsibly, ethically and to a high scientific standard, in order to find treatment for disease as early as possible.

ETHICS IN DAILY PRACTICE

Although the public debate on ethics is limited to a handful of hot topics, including stem cell research, the potential application of ethical principles is very broad. The field of ethics informs general problem-solving approaches. It provides a way of looking at the world of clinical practice and healthcare based on a given set of values and principles.

It is not necessary to be a specialist steeped in the concepts and schools of ethical thought to appreciate ethical dimensions of daily medical practice. The fundamental ethical principle in the delivery of healthcare is respect for the individual patient.

The nature of the doctor-patient relationship was once captured in idealised form by the popular American illustrator Norman Rockwell. In 1947, the artist's creation *Norman Rockwell Visits a Family Doctor* (see figure 2, page 66)[3] appeared in the US publication *The Saturday Evening Post*.

The illustration presents the quintessential doctor of the imagination. It captures the solidarity between the doctor and the family: their concerns are his concerns. The doctor's office is depicted in warm colours. All of the elements of the image – the dog, the rocking chair, the glowing fire and the old hat – exude reassurance, familiarity and stability.

From time to time, Rockwell depicted medical subjects but few captured the idealised essence of family doctoring so powerfully.

This romantic illustration of the good doctor grew out of the small-town American experience but could easily have pertained to the National Health Service (NHS) in Britain in the middle of the 20th century.

In the UK, a similarly noble image of the doctor was presented by Sir George Pickering, who was then Regius Professor of Medicine at Oxford University, in his presidential address to a British Medical Association meeting in 1963.

In the address, titled *Manners Makyth Man: A Plea for the Importance of Character in Medicine*, Sir George said:

> Unless the doctor is utterly devoted to his patients and prepared to take immense trouble to understand their problems, he is inferior to a machine. It is only by virtue of that rather intangible and neglected quality, his attitude of mind as expressed by devotion to his patient, the real ethos of Medicine, that he becomes superior.[4]

CONCERN ABOUT POOR DOCTORS

The Rockwell illustration and the Pickering address exemplify traditional views of the practice of medicine. In the past, goodness in medical practice was seen as the commitment all doctors make to practising in a way that displays care, compassion and the conscientious exercise of highly developed professional skills.

From the 1950s through to the 1970s, medicine was practised according to a broad professional code. Professionals were accountable to individual patients and also to a set of ethical principles and standards of conduct that were not clearly defined.

Like many healthcare systems founded in the mid-20th century, the NHS in Britain, which was established in 1948, originally had no explicit programmes to address quality assurance and quality improvement. Quality was taken for granted and the notion of a 'bad doctor' was rarely encountered.

In the post-establishment years, there were some early signs of dissatisfaction with the quality of service from within the medic world.

For example, in the 1960s, a slim volume called *Deplorable Doctors*, by Dr R. Maplesden Pearce was published.[5] The dust jacket read: 'Most doctors are honest. Most of them carry out their work conscientiously and efficiently …'

However, the text went on, the 'profession is besmirched', by the minority of doctors who can truthfully be described as 'deplorable'.

Unusual for its time, the book presented a series of anecdotes, reflections and assertions about anonymous 'bad' doctors.

Figure 2: *Norman Rockwell Visits a Family Doctor* (1947).

ATTITUDES TO STANDARDS

By the 1980s, the 'bad doctor' was a more familiar concept and personal notions about the relationship between the doctor and the need to be more explicit about standards of practice gained recognition.

The growth of managed care led to a more official, contractual form of accountability. The rise of management in health care drove the need for doctors and other health professionals to be accountable for their services within the corporate structures of hospitals and other health organizations.

The General Medical Council, the UK's main regulatory body for medicine, began to set out much more explicit criteria for the ethical basis of practice. Accountability in medicine moved from a broad professional code to a set of more explicit boundaries on professional and clinical autonomy.

In the 1990s, the new evidence-based medicine movement created an expectation that more clinical decisions would be based on proven practices and products. This movement came in response to two main problems: variation in clinical decision-making and slow uptake of effective interventions.

The 1990s were also marked by the emergence of patients' rights and guarantees, particularly in relation to waiting times.

The media's influence on public perceptions was potent. News outlets began to hold health service providers responsible for incidents involving poor standards of care that resulted in patient harm. Incidents and events illustrating seriously bad care within local health services became public in a way that would not have been conceivable in the early years of the National Health Service.

In the aggressive, investigative media environment of the late 20th century, patients' deaths were no longer viewed as mishaps or unfortunate accidents, but as scandals. The plight of the victim was highlighted and blame and accountability were pinned firmly on those perceived as responsible.

Well-publicised scandals about lapses in standards in care in UK health institutions contributed to the erosion of public confidence. Most notoriously, in the early 1990s an inquiry exposed poor standards of care in the Bristol Royal Infirmary's children's heart surgery service.[6] In that case, long-standing problems with unusually high mortality rates following operative procedures at Bristol, belatedly came to the attention of the public through the actions of a whistle-blower. (*See Professor Sir Ian Kennedy's contribution to this volume.*)

SYSTEMIC PROBLEMS

Throughout the last decade of the 20th century, many doctors said they felt beleaguered in the glare of a hostile media spotlight. They also felt that the entire profession was being blamed for the mistakes of a small number of individuals.

However, investigations of problem doctor cases in the UK in the 1990s revealed serious systemic problems and broader responsibility for poor practice. In some cases, problems with individual doctors had been known and discussed by other professionals via informal channels for years, yet no one had been willing or able to take decisive action to amend these situations.

An investigation of Dr Rodney Ledward, the rogue gynaecologist, is a case in point. By the time he was barred after 30-plus years in practice, he allegedly had committed numerous offences, including the removal of ovaries from a woman without informed consent, and botched operations.

Some of those on the inside of the healthcare establishment had known about problems with Dr Ledward's practice for years, whereas those on the outside – including his patients – were left unaware and uninformed.

Failure to act against a fellow professional may result from the subordination of patient safety and/or the patient's interest to other concerns, such as professional loyalty, avoidance of litigation and fear of bad publicity. Whatever the rationale, failure to act on problem doctors has clearly left patients at risk. It has denied patients the respect they deserve.

PATIENT RIGHTS GAIN PROMINENCE

Whereas in the past, the doctor was expected to know best when it came to clinical decisions, today, many rightfully believe the patient's voice should be absolutely central in healthcare.

The point was well illustrated by writer and disability rights activist Micheline Mason in the early 1980s. After hearing a debate about pre-natal screening and the withdrawal of medical treatment of newborn infants with impairments, Micheline, who was born in 1950 with a congenital disability, was moved to share her own experience, in a letter to the magazine *Child: care, health and development*, she attempted to communicate the voice of the child who would later be a disabled adult, as well as the long-term effects of attitudes and decisions made by medical staff on behalf of young disabled people.

Micheline wrote: 'A message clearly and firmly slipped into my unconscious that people would prefer it if I died…. I have spent nearly all my time desperately trying to prove that I should be alive, that I was not suffering (even when I was) and that I was not worthless, but indeed exceptionally worthwhile. This meant that everything I did had to be outstanding. I am now 30 years old. Only now am I beginning to realise that I do not have to smile all the time, and that I can achieve mediocrity without feeling someone will come and put me out of my misery.'[7]

Similarly, UK Disability Rights Commissioner Jane Campbell, who has a neuromuscular disease called spinal muscular atrophy (SMA) has spoken eloquently about her struggle to prove her own worth to the outside world.[8]

Following diagnosis when Jane was just a few days old, her mother was told to take her home and enjoy her, as she would die within a year. Fortunately, the doctors were wrong. Throughout her life, Jane has frequently been unwell with chest infections but it has been possible to manage her condition through treatment with antibiotics and ventilation.

At one point, she developed pneumonia and was taken to hospital. Jane recalls hearing doctors discussing her case and assuming that she would not want treatment if she lost consciousness. They had placed a value on her life. She forced herself to stay awake for 48 hours, fearful of the consequences of falling asleep whilst seriously ill and distrustful of doctors' intentions.

During a hospital, her husband brought with him a framed photograph of Jane in a wheelchair at her university graduation ceremony. He then threw the photograph on her bed in front of the attending doctors and said, 'Treat the person you see in the photograph, not what you think you see in the bed.'

With those words, Jane's husband challenged the balance of power between doctors and patients in the delivery of quality medical care.

LESSONS FROM ALDER HEY

Lack of balance of power between professionals and patients was also highlighted in the scandal that erupted in the late 1990s over organ retention in the absence of informed consent. At that time, reports about the harvesting of body parts from dead children at three children's hospitals, including the Alder Hey Children's Hospital in Liverpool, caused an uproar and spurred demands for reform.

Some pathologists have acknowledged that even setting aside the extreme practices of organ retention at Alder Hey, there has generally been an inappropriate approach to taking and storing organs and tissues.

In the past, there was an unqualified acceptance of the need to support the greater good of research and education without, in some cases, enough consideration for the needs of families of those who have died.

In January 2001, the issue of organ retention was discussed at a meeting attended by medical professionals and relatives of children whose body parts had been removed and retained. At times, emotions ran high.

One parent said: 'When a child dies, that child is still the parent's child, not a specimen, not a cause, not an unfortunate casualty of a failed procedure, but someone's baby, someone's child. In life, the parent is responsible for every aspect of a child's well being. In death, that responsibility should not be taken away.'[9] (Stephen Parker, Bristol Heart Children's Action Group)

At the end of the meeting, a number of doctors said that up until that point, they had never understood the depth of feeling a parent had for a child's body after death. Some said that their attitudes towards patients would never be the same again.

HUMAN TISSUE BILL

Reports and inquiries have shown that storage and use of organs and tissue from both adults and children without proper consent was widespread in the past. It also became clear that the current law in this area was not comprehensive, nor as clear and consistent as it might be for professionals or the families involved.

Following extensive consultation with public and professionals, in December

2003 the Government published the Human Tissue Bill[†], which will extend to England, Wales and Northern Ireland.[10]

The purpose of the Human Tissue Bill is to provide a consistent legislative framework for issues relating to whole body donation and the taking, storage and use of human organs and tissue. It will establish consent as the fundamental principle underpinning the lawful removal of material from the bodies of the dead, as well as storage and use of human bodies, body parts, organs and tissue.

It will set up an over-arching authority to rationalize existing regulation of activities such as transplantation and anatomical examination. This authority will also introduce regulation of other activities like post-mortem examinations and the storage of human material for education, training and research. The legislation is intended to achieve a balance between the rights and expectations of individuals and families versus broader considerations, such as the importance of research, education, training and public health surveillance to the population as a whole.

This new, comprehensive framework may help restore public and professional confidence in the donation and use of tissue and organs.

HEALTH SYSTEM REFORM

A broader initiative is underway to restore public confidence in the UK health system as a whole.

In the 1990s, the UK Government, the NHS and the medical profession embarked on a radical programme of clinical governance to improve standards and protect patients in the future. Starting in the late 1990s, a statutory duty of quality was placed on every health organization. Consequently, every local health service is now required to introduce quality assurance and quality improvement programmes.

In 2000, the Department of Health published a report called *An organisation with a memory*.[11] According to the report, problems in the NHS were linked to the lack of reliable means of identifying, analysing and systematically learning from serious lapses in standards of care. In the past, there was no clear path for introducing change on the local level at problem sites and throughout the health service to prevent similar events occurring again.

Today, the NHS understands much more about poor practitioner performance and has mechanisms for early identification and rigorous assessment of problems, as well as solutions. If these mechanisms are functioning properly, patients will not be exposed to unnecessary risk for long periods. Contrary to the traditional model for professional oversight, which was based on negativity and punishment, impaired performance is now viewed as a problem to be fixed and failures will be dealt with openly and constructively.

Since 2000, the General Medical Council has been undergoing the most comprehensive reform of professional registration since establishment in 1858. The reforms are designed to make the GMC become more effective,

---

† *This became the Human Tissue Act 2004, with a commencement date of 2005.*

inclusive and accountable. For example, the GMC has introduced 'revalidation' for physician registration. From 2005, doctors must demonstrate that they meet the standards required for registration every five years.

The Government has also set out to create a culture conducive to improving patient safety. In 2001, it created the National Patient Safety Agency (NPSA), a Special Health Authority to co-ordinate efforts to report and learn from adverse incidents in the NHS. A key role of the agency is to encourage health professionals to report breaches of safety even if they have only resulted in a 'near miss'. An estimated 850,000 incidents occur every year, accounting for about one in ten hospital admissions.

In 2004, the NPSA launched the National Reporting and Learning System (NLRS), a national anonymous reporting system that will allow the gathering and sharing of experience with adverse events across the National Health Service.

Extensive study in the non-health field shows that with most unintended failures there is usually no single explanatory cause for the event. Rather there is a complex interaction between a variety of elements including human behaviour, technological conditions, socio-cultural factors and a range of organisational and management weaknesses.

Following the implementation of a number of substantive reforms, serious adverse events in the NHS continue to occur and reinforce the need for further action, including changes to the design and safety features of medical devices, as well as the packaging and labelling of medicines.

FOCUSING ON THE PATIENT

Reformers have also introduced clear channels of communication between patients and professionals, via the newly established Commission for Patient and Public Involvement in Health.

This organization has set up independent Patient and Public Involvement (PPI) Forums, groups that gather feedback about healthcare services on the regional and local levels. As of the end of 2003, there were nearly 600 PPI fora across England involving more than 4,000 people. The Commission has also established Independent Complaints Advocacy Services which accept and manage problems in the National Health Service. Information from these locally operated bodies is shared with officials in central Government, as well as the national Healthcare Commission, the new healthcare inspection and standards body.

Consumers may also obtain help and information through Patient Advice and Liaison Services (PALS), which are operated by Primary Care Trusts.

PAST, PRESENT AND FUTURE

Medicine as a profession and the National Health Service as an institution have changed a great deal since Lord Jakobovits began to write and lecture on medical ethics in the 1940s.

Good quality care is now judged in explicit ways. Doctors and other health professionals at all levels of organizations must embrace the need not just to deliver care but to think about quality and safety as integral parts of their everyday work.

We now understand that there are very few bad people in our health services but that professionals can and do sometimes deliver bad healthcare. In these cases, failures are often related to weaknesses of systems, processes, culture and leadership within health services.

The traditional balance of power in the relationship between health professional and patient has been reoriented in favour of the patient and there will be no reversal of this trend. Increasingly, patients are being asked to help define quality of services, participate in decisions about their care and guide improvements in services. Patients deserve access to the latest in technology, but not at the expense of the human side of healthcare.

The concept of respect elucidated by Rabbi Jakobovits and other great thinkers in medical ethics must not be seen as a narrow strand of professional etiquette but rather as an issue of immense proportion.

In the new world of clinical practice and healthcare, the important principle of respect can be seen in holistic terms. Respect for patients goes beyond the individual relationship between health professional and patient. Respect means creating the right organisational culture, embedding the right professional standards and values throughout a health system and instilling the right philosophy about service to a patient.

Only by embedding respect in our system at the level of the individual encounter and throughout the national institutional fabric, will our health service move away from some of the paternalistic patterns of the past and assume its position among the best systems in the world.

NOTES

[1] Rosner, F. (2001) 'Lord Immanuel Jakobovits: Grandfather of Jewish Medical Ethics', *Israel Medical Association Journal* 3, 304–310.

[2] Jakobovits, I. (1966) 'Medical experimentation on humans in Jewish Law', *Proceedings of the Association of Orthodox Jewish Scientists, New York 1966* Vol 1. Reprinted in Rosner, F. and Bleich, J.D. (eds) *Jewish Bioethics* (New York, Sanhedrin Press, 1979), 377–83.

[3] Donaldson, U. (2002) 'Norman Rockwell visits a family doctor', *Clinical Medicine* 2(3), 266.

[4] Pickering, G. (1963) 'Manners Makyth Man: A Plea for the Importance of Character in Medicine', Presidential Address, British Medical Association. *British Medical Journal* 5350, 133–5.

[5] Pearce, R.M. (1965) *Deplorable Doctors* (London, Hutchinson).

[6] Kennedy, I. (2001) *Learning from Bristol: the Report of the Public Inquiry into Children's Heart Surgery at the Bristol Royal Infirmary 1984–1995* (London, The Stationery Office).

[7] Mason, M. (1981) 'Correspondence', *Child: care, health and development* 7, 183–6.

[8] Campbell, J. (2003) 'Don't be fooled: we don't all want to kill ourselves', *The Independent* (21 January), 17; and personal communication.

[9] Department of Health (2001) *The Removal, Retention and Use of Human Organs and Tissue from Post-mortem Examination* (London, The Stationery Office).

[10] See reference in Lord Woolf's contribution, to the Government's intention to combine the regulatory functions of the HFEA with those of the Human Tissue Authority into a Single Regulatory Authority for Tissue and Embryos (Queen's Speech, November 2006).

[11] Department of Health (2002) *An organisation with a memory: report of an expert group on learning from adverse events in the NHS* (London, The Stationery Office).

MEDICAL ETHICS –
A SURGEON'S PERSPECTIVE

Santilal Parbhoo*
Cancerkin, Royal Free Hospital and Hospital of St John
and St Elizabeth, London

Medical ethics provides guidelines for the practice of medicine. There is a need for listening, caring, understanding and respect for the human condition alongside the application of technical skill and scientific knowledge. Respect for the human being and dead body has been practised for thousands of years from ancient Babylonian, Egyptian, Indian, Greek and Jewish traditions. This respect for the body and its parts may now be focussed on smaller parts such as the embryo, cell and subcellular structures such as chromosomes, which carry the genes. The moral guidelines were traditionally set out in the Hippocratic Oath introduced by Hippocrates (c.460–c.370 BC). The revised 'Christianized' version has been used in European medical schools and in schools in countries under European colonial rule. Technological advances have sometimes caused doctors to lose

* Santilal Parbhoo MB, ChB, PhD, FRCS

Santilal Parbhoo was born in and completed his undergraduate training in Cape Town. He came to advance his surgical training as a British Council Scholar in the United Kingdom between 1962 and 1964 and then as a surgical trainee in Belfast, London, Bristol and Leuven. In 1974 he was appointed Consultant Surgeon and Senior Lecturer and was Chairman of the Division of Surgery at the Royal Free Hospital (1987–9) and Chairman of the Board of Surgical Studies (1984–91)

He is a founder member of the Ludwig International Breast Cancer Study Group, a NATO International Research Travelling Fellow and was a member of various committees associated with the UK Breast Screening Programme. He is a member of the executive committee of the International Society of Lymphology and a member of the British Lymphology Society. He is a member of the Scientific Advisory Committee of the International Society of Lymphology, Europa Donna UK Forum and Cancerkin. He was instrumental in developing the multi-disciplinary Royal Free Hospital Breast Unit from 1978. In 1987 he co-founded and has co-developed Cancerkin, an internationally recognised Breast Patients Support Service which established the first dedicated Lymphoedema Clinic for breast cancer patients in the UK.

At various times he has been visiting Professor to the Universities of Milan, Amman, Cairo, Tanta, Cape Town and the Gaslini Institute, Genoa.

His research interests and publications have included the following topics: – diagnosis of breast cancer, bone metastases, biology of breast cancer, lymphoedema, breast conservation surgery, imaging recurrent breast cancer, sentinel lymph node biopsy, understanding the normal breast.

His breast practice is international with regular consultations from 30 countries. He is currently Lead Consultant Breast Surgeon at the Hospital of St John and St Elizabeth and Medical Director of Cancerkin.

their objectivity, art and humanity in the practice of medicine. Indeed, superspecialization has led some doctors to focus on a particular problem or organ without viewing the patient as a whole.

MORALITY AND MEDICAL DECISION MAKING

Doctors may have to walk the moral maze when the patient's and medical attendant's perceptions differ. What the doctor thinks is good for the patient and humanity (society or community) may not coincide with the patient's best interests.[1] The best management decisions for two patients with exactly the same disease may be quite different and yet correct and appropriate. The differences may be due to the different situations relating to the patient, clinical experience and 'morality' of the doctor and guidelines from medical and governmental organisations such as the General Medical Council (GMC), Royal Colleges and National Institute of Clinical Excellence (NICE). J. K. Mason's editorial makes the point succinctly when he states that 'ethical medical practice is ultimately developed in the consulting room and at the bedside'.[2] When society lacks a firm moral basis and doctors follow legislation, only a change in law can reform that society. The medical apartheid operated by doctors within the confines of South African law extended even to the use of racially classified blood for transfusion. The abolition of racist laws was required to obtain equity of medical care.

'BETWEEN YOU AND ME'

Patient confidentiality relates to confidentiality of information given to doctors during the course of a medical consultation. There are many arguments in favour of preserving confidentiality. If a patient worries that personal information may be divulged, they will co-operate less. During consultation there is an implicit agreement of confidentiality which is one of the most cherished aspects in the relationship between patient and doctor and is based on trust. An absence of confidentiality will ultimately damage self-determination and privacy. For centuries the doctor has also been the father confessor of patients. Much of this relationship is changing. Patients expect to be able to trust their doctor not to divulge private information. Equally, doctors expect their patients to provide full information. Some very personal and private information may help in the diagnosis of an ailment. Even more important is that the lack of detail or misleading information may lead to a wrong diagnosis and potentially dangerous treatment. However, the principle of confidentiality is not absolute and can be forced to give way to the 'public interest' in disclosure.[3]

In general practice and more so in hospitals or institutions, medicine is practised as a team effort. Many specialized areas of medicine need multidisciplinary discussion involving groups of medical and para-medical hospital personnel who all contribute to the discussion and decision regarding the diagnosis and management of the patient. In this technological age the vast amount of information gathered on a patient now appears on computer monitors which may or may not provide secure confidentiality. Each NHS Trust now has to have a Caldicott Guardian who is responsible for maximizing patient confidentiality.[4] In practice, this may vary from removal of notices identifying patients in the ward from public places to ensuring adequate protection of patients in publications relating to them.

Publication of medical papers often involves providing the results of clinical research, discussion of unusual cases, reports of cases studies or information on new technology and operative procedures. Many publications are now posted on the Internet for medical and allied professions. However, access to these sites may be made by the lay public and just as in the case of access to medical journals, newsheets etc., patients may recognize themselves as involved in the case report or clinical study. Special consent from the patient is now required prior to publication of case reports. Patients may claim or feel that they are violated because private matters discussed with a doctor have reached the public domain. The issue of privacy applies both to the patient and authors. Large studies involving thousands of patients in multicentre studies across the globe will involve distribution of clinical and personal data. Accurate information that can be validated is essential to prevent bogus entry of patients into trials. This requires careful ethical consideration of the studies and appropriate patient consent. Where the data have been anonymized, they can and should be used in research without consent. The use of this type of information in meta-analyses has led to the recognition of small but significant differences in outcome, which changes future medical management.

'DO WHATEVER YOU THINK IS NECESSARY DOC!'

Modern consent to medical treatment requires informed consent. How much information should the patient be given regarding the diagnosis, procedure and operation? The precise legal criteria are unclear and distinguished judges disagree (see the 3–2 decision in the House of Lords in the case of *Chester v Afshar*).[5] The plethora of information and advice available to doctors has led to further uncertainty. After providing all the information one should give the patient an opportunity to ask questions. It is advisable that information given to the patient should be documented in the medical records. The doctor needs to ensure that the patient is legally and mentally able to consent and that no undue influence has been brought to bear by professional staff or relatives which would vitiate the patient's consent to treatment. Doctors often have to make a value judgement as to the mental capacity and competence of the patient to understand the information provided. Informed consent entails provision of details about the medication or procedure, disclosure of significant risk and alternative options. It is essential that doctors and the public need to have a better understanding of the nature of risk. Patients can become unnecessarily worried or terrified of adverse effects or post-operative complications if they have been given a bland list of adverse effects or complications in a leaflet without information of the likelihood of these unwanted effects. Doctors have to make a value judgement taking into consideration the patient's ability to understand, their level of education, language, beliefs, and culture when obtaining consent. While this may be difficult, it is essential to take these aspects into account when obtaining valid consent.

Consent to treatment may either be expressed or implied. Legally, both verbal and written consent is equally valid. For minor procedures such as taking the blood pressure or venepuncture, the mere co-operation of the patient is legally valid as implied consent. In patients with mental handicap and mental illness, the capacity to consent has to be assessed in relation to specific procedures or treatment. They may understand and consent to simple procedures but one may not be able to obtain informed consent for complex management. Again, the law has pronounced on these difficulties and constructed what is known as the three stage test – in *Re C* in that the patient: (i) needs to have the capacity to comprehend and retain information; (ii) believe the information; and (iii) weigh the information in the balance and choose.[6] United Kingdom law recognizes a 'best interests' test for vulnerable patients.[7]

It is generally agreed that doctors may give emergency treatment in life threatening situations in the best interests of the patient without consent. In the intensive care unit (ITU) situation it is appropriate for the medical and nursing team to approach relatives and obtain their agreement to the management plan once the patient has been stabilized after the acute event which caused the patient to be admitted to the ITU. Where patients are admitted to the ITU as part of their post-operative course, this situation should have been explained to the patient and relative or partner as part of the pre-operative information giving and consent procedure.

Who should obtain consent? This was often left to the most junior doctor in the team who may have little knowledge of the procedure and its complications. In the context of pre-surgery consultation, it is essential that the surgeon carrying out the operation should explain the intended procedure and provide the associated information prior to obtaining consent. In complex procedures, the consent process can occur over some time so that both patient and surgeon can have time to discuss the procedures in details as appropriate to the patient and procedure.[8,9] Patients may need to be aware that information about themselves (appropriately disguised) may be used in research and certainly as part of the audit process.

Modern consent to surgical procedures should include reference to actual or potential research with regard to the tissue examined or stored for their personal benefit or for the greater good (see below).

As the public becomes more aware of 'outcome' data they will request this information at the time of consent. Good audit is therefore an essential element of the doctor's ability to provide honest and useful information to the patient.

'WHO GETS WHAT'

Resources and medical ethics

Traditionally, wealthy populations had better access to the best medicine available. In modern times, the well-off or insured population has a better access to a wider spectrum of treatment or perhaps better medicine. National programmes such as the National Health Service (NHS) have striven to provide more equitable health services. Divides remain in how the national resources are distributed. Whereas the 'Western world' is concerned with modern and exciting medicine, many other parts of the world have to justify performing expensive sophisticated surgery on a few with perhaps limited life. Thus the expectations of the patient in the developed world may be in competition with the great need for more primary care centres for large parts of the population who do not have access to medical services. The explosion of science and technology in the medical arena has led to higher costs and increased public expectations. The medical profession has to shoulder some of the blame of fuelling unreasonable expectations, which may take decades to reach the public by making inflated claims on the basis of research. Gene therapy is one area where the public perception and hope have been mistaken due to poor information and lack of education of the public by doctors. Since resources are limited and demands theoretically infinite, there has to be some system of resource allocation (rationing). Cost effectiveness of health care and use of drugs and surgery becomes even more important as costs spiral and needs become infinite. Doctors need to play a part in public education regarding alternative and complementary medicine, which are playing an increasing and costly role. These para and pseudomedical treatments need to be as rigorously evaluated as are standard medical treatments. In an ideal world all members of society requiring medical attention will get appropriate, correct and adequate treatment. Because of the development of medicine in many spheres – diagnosis, treatment, prevention and prophylaxis – there will be discussion and argument about who decides how and where the service and help is delivered. Doctors, together with society, need to be able to achieve agreement as to what constitutes acceptable rationing or discrimination. While patients have the right to accept or refuse treatment, they must also be made aware of their responsibility for health. In the USA plans are afoot to attempt imposing personal responsibility in health care as part of the Medicaid Reform for the uninsured population.[10] While the concept of personal responsibility is laudable, imposition of credits and punitive measures is in conflict with the doctor–patient relationship.[11]

Governments need to work with doctors and society to prevent alienation and to reach some form of consensus to provide healthcare and best quality of life for the majority of the population. Inevitably the system must cater for some special cases and any derived system must have the inbuilt flexibility to provide doctors with the mechanism of providing 'special care' for a few unusual situations. Rationing does affect the doctor's fundamental duty to treat the patient according to his best clinical judgement and experience.

However, evidence based medicine should provide better medicine for the greater good. This implies that doctors may be ethical utilitarians in principle and practice by force of circumstance.

As an example, doctors have to make painful decisions as to the use of certain limited facilities such as incubators or intensive care beds when a number of patients require similar treatment. While scarce resources should be allotted on the presumed medical benefit, it may be difficult to ration medical treatment on this basis alone. Many factors have to be considered in reaching a consensus for securing treatment, as prognosis in these very difficult cases is very uncertain.

Many common diseases in large populations go untreated and little attempt is made to prevent diseases as they occur in parts of the world where real or potential patients are unable to pay for the funding of medical and pharmaceutical research required to develop and manufacture effective and appropriate drugs. The manufacture of medicines is an expensive, high-risk enterprise and therefore global efforts will be required to address this issue. Doctors cannot shy away from the responsibility of providing good medicine to all the world's peoples. It is part of our ethical duty to convince medical academics and pharmaceutical industries that the global elimination of disease and care for all, is good medicine and good politics!

'A GOOD DEATH'

Euthanasia is the act of taking life to relieve suffering and is derived from the Greek words *eu* (good) and *thanatos* (death).

The Bill proposed by the human rights lawyer, Lord Joffe would enable adults who are terminally ill, suffering unbearably and of sound mind to request assistance to die, i.e. voluntary euthanasia. This would entail the doctor providing the patient with a lethal drug to administer to himself or herself. Doctors and the lay public are worried that this law legalizing euthanasia might put undue pressure on the patient not to be a 'burden' on relatives or society. A recent (2006) Royal College of Physicians (London) survey amongst colleagues found that the majority opposed a change in the law which would legalize 'mercy killing.' This medical view is at variance with the general public view, which is in favour of euthanasia. The majority of the Fellows felt that 'with improvements in palliative care, good clinical care can be provided within existing legislation and that patients can die with dignity.' The opposite argument is that in practice 'assisted' deaths are part and parcel of palliative medicine when doctors and their patients come to a decision that there is no future in extending life. Many will argue that the law as it stands permits 'assisted' deaths without accountability and without regard to safeguards. The BBC programme 'A good death' by Esther Rantzen has done much to highlight the problems of death and stimulated public debate. Death is the final event in the process of dying. The programme made it clear that the process of dying is not understood by most of the population. It is difficult for doctors because of their training and the family because of their connection to the patient not to view death as an admission of failure. Most of us would like to be able to choose when and where to die. The programme summarized the needs of the dying – to be with family and friends, to be pain free, to maintain their dignity, to have privacy and peace, to have good information about their illness and treatment. Patients must be informed about and given options for making living wills. Doctors can do much attending to the needs of the dying in the hospice and less so in the hospital and home setting. We must, however, strive to do better within the available resources

ALLOWING NATURE TO TAKE ITS COURSE

Doctors may be criticized both for resuscitating and for not doing so. The mere availability of techniques or equipment to keep patients alive should not be the reason for inappropriate resuscitation. One of the most difficult decisions doctors have to make is whether an attempt is made to carry out cardiopulmonary resuscitation (CPR) on a particular patient. Ideally the decision should be taken after discussion with the attending team and the patient if he is competent, or the relatives if the patient is incompetent.

The Do Not Attempt Resuscitation (DNAR) order is based on the premise that it is in the best interests of the patient. It should be noted in the patient's records. Most hospitals will also have rules as to how long it should be in force and how often the order has to be updated. Doctors are not required to give what they would consider as inappropriate treatments when the outcome is likely to be futile. There is public misconception about DNAR orders. It is important to emphasize that DNAR does not mean 'do not treat.' The public should also know that more than 90 per cent of in hospital resuscitation attempts are unsuccessful. The DNAR decision made by an individual doctor may be a great burden. Ideally the treating team should make the decision. The decision is based on a number of ethical considerations – including patient autonomy, the clinician's duty to treat, or not to give futile treatment, the views of clinical colleagues and the value and quality of life.

'DESIGNER BABIES AND POPULATIONS'

Eugenics is the science that is concerned mainly with the detection, and where possible, the elimination of genetic disease in man.

The best known consequences of modern attempts to improve the gene pool has been the development of screening procedures for various 'inborn' abnormalities. Until recently, a screening procedure, known as pre-implantation genetic diagnosis (PGD) was approved in cases of conditions where the mutations led to at least a 90 per cent chance of developing a disease. However in May 2006, the Human Fertilisation and Embryology Authority (HFEA) authorised the screening of embryos during IVF treatment. See Baroness Deech's contribution to this volume. A single cell will be removed from the embryo for testing for breast and colon cancer genes – BRCA1, BRCA2 and HNPCC in women who carry these genes. Only embryos without these genes would be used. Previously the authority (HFEA) had granted licences to permit screening of embryos where the chance of being affected would be in the order of 90 per cent such as certain forms of colon cancer and the eye cancer – retinoblastoma. There is concern that the more recent move may lead to gradually increasing the indications for screening for less serious genetic traits.

Later testing or screening of the foetus is offered to older parents where the risk of conditions such as Down's syndrome and spina bifida are higher. Modern ultrasound scanning provides early information on some of these conditions. Earlier examination of amniotic fluid may provide further information regarding the likelihood of these problems. Amniocentesis (withdrawal of amniotic fluid) provides shed foetal cells, which can be analysed for chromosomal, or biochemical abnormalities. The prenatal diagnosis of these abnormalities legally permits termination of the abnormal foetus.

Reduction of multiple pregnancy

In cases of multiple pregnancy with IVF, some embryos have been retained for stem cell research and possible later use for implantation. This allows for the greater survival of the selected embryos to full term. Orthodox religious groups may hold that this 'culling' of embryos is immoral, irreligious and murder, despite the fact that none or only a few might survive if one allowed nature to take its course.

How far we go down this road of selection and destruction is very unclear. There are many who value human life per se, whatever its physical or intellectual potential or defects.

ABORTION – A CLASH OF INTERESTS

Abortion is the removal of an embryo or foetus from the uterus at a stage of pregnancy when it is incapable of independent survival. Induced abortion for medical or psychological reasons (termination of pregnancy) is legal in the UK provided it has been carried out under the terms of the Abortion Act 1967 and subsequent Abortion Regulations 1991. A useful distinction used by the lay public and increasingly recognized by doctors is that abortion relates to a deliberate procedure or medication to end pregnancy as opposed to miscarriage where abortion has occurred spontaneously. In certain religious circles the prevention of implantation of the fertilized ovum, by the use of 'the morning after pill' is also regarded as abortion. Much of the religious argument is based on the mysticism and discussion as to when the soul enters the human embryo or body. Some religions believe that the soul enters the potential embryo at the time of conception, therefore indicating that a human being is present. The Talmudic view expressed by Lord Jakobovits is that when most of the foetus is outside the womb or according to some versions, when the head has emerged from the birth canal, it may be considered as a human person and has the rights of a human being.[12] Glover has discussed the lessons to be learned from the abortion debate.[13] Much argument revolves around the rights of the mother and the foetus. The extreme pro-life view is that the fertilized egg or the embryo is a person or human being with the same rights as us, which would mean that the morning after pill is the same as murder. In the opposite corner are 'pro-choice' advocates who believe that the only moral issue is the woman's right to control her body. Glover indicates that the extreme positions are the result of a reluctance to accept moral complexity and ambiguity. As time marches on and as we increase our knowledge about the natural development of the foetus we are becoming less rigid in our attitudes.

Nature is the greatest cause of abortions. Abnormal foetuses are recognized and disposed of naturally by the pregnant mother. Increasingly, as we become more aware of the actual and potential abnormalities in individual foetuses by testing the amniotic fluid, maternal and foetal blood (and even individual cells from embryos during in vitro fertilization) we can eliminate certain diseases or abnormalities. Moral dilemmas occur for the patient. She requires careful, sympathetic advice as in the case of abortion of a genetically abnormal foetus for a Roman Catholic, or a possibly normal foetus in a case of rape. Groups representing the disabled in society have made a strong argument for the protection and rights of the foetus with potential disability. In affluent societies such as the West, disabled people can be cared for and enjoy a good quality of life. In many parts of the world, however, the birth of a disabled child may bring added misfortune and untold misery on a family. The financial situation of a society and the culture into which the disabled child may be born are important considerations for the society and attending doctors.

HUMAN EXPERIMENTATION

The expansion and need for human experimentation has led to the development of Ethics Committees in hospitals, medical institutions and medical schools whose task it is to assess this activity and provide guidance to the research workers. These committees consist of experts and lay persons concerned with teaching and research involving the use of human subjects. Their role is to ensure that adequate basic research has been carried out prior to human experimentation; that adequate information is available regarding the project; that there is sufficient understanding of procedures; that the experimentation is safe; that there are safeguards and treatment if things go wrong; that there is adequate compensation; and that no one is pressurised or coerced into participating. Importantly they have to be satisfied that the research is likely to yield useful results. The experiments may involve the development of new techniques of diagnosis, screening, surgery or drugs. Rapidly advancing technology in diagnosis, manipulation of the body and body parts has raised questions as to how far we should intervene in the natural process.

Drug trials

Drug trials are an essential element in the development of drugs. Trials are required to assess the efficacy, potency and duration of action as well as adverse side effects. Thousands of patients may be required for some trials to be able to measure small beneficial effects, which may still have a major impact on a disease. It is estimated that one per cent of all hospital beds in the UK are occupied by patients as a result of medical adverse reactions. Since this was written the drug trial mishap at Northwick Park Hospital has occurred. Apart from the human misery, doctors have to consider that the unwanted side effects are expensive and prevent treatment of other patients.

Although billions of pounds are spent on alternative and complementary medicines and treatments, few scientific studies are available to ensure the safety and efficacy of these agents or activities. Doctors and their regulatory authorities have generally steered clear of the minefield of problems associated with possible regulation of the 'para-medical' and pseudo-scientific potions and procedures but this needs to change. Furthermore, some very good medicines may be developed as a result of investigating 'folk-lore medicines', remedies from distant cultures and witchdoctor medicines.

Stem cell research

At times the principles of 'do no harm' and 'do good' are in conflict, as in the reduction of multiple embryos or even foetuses. The eliminated embryo or foetus is harmed for the benefit or survival of the remaining embryos or foetus. The use of aborted foetuses for research and transplantation was approved in 1989 in the UK. This farsighted legislation has permitted the development of stem cell research, which may greatly enhance our ability to understand and treat congenital disorders and promote advances in tissue transplantation.

'FOR THE GREATER GOOD'

Population treatments

All medical interventions be they physical, medical or psychological will have side effects. When this is applied to large parts of the population, due care has to be taken to ensure that the benefits outweigh the problems and side effects of any activity. Screening to detect disease (e.g. UK breast screening and cervical screening programmes) may, in some instances, have unforeseen side effects. 'Normal' people become 'patients' and may undergo unnecessary invasive procedures and even operations. What is important is that these side effects are within acceptable levels and that the situation can be remedied. As with immunization, screening programmes will work and be beneficial for the population provided the uptake of screening is at a sufficiently high level to maintain viability of the programme. The UK Breast Screening Programme has been a national success story despite the difficulties and lack of resources. It does, however, lead to a number of unnecessary operations on patients who have benign breast changes only. Other programmes, such as whole body CT scanning for the worried well have dubious medical benefits and may carry serious radiation side effects.

Education of the population

An essential aspect of good medicine is the prevention of ill health. Immunization, vaccination, reduction in traffic accidents, reduction of occupational hazards, improvement in the environment all have a major role in the prevention of ill-health.

Immunization

Immunization is one of the most effective and economic public health programmes to improve the health of the nation. Eradication of the scourge of smallpox worldwide has been one of the great success stories of immunization. Similarly the prevalence of many serious diseases has been dramatically reduced. Uptake of the programme needs to be at a high level to provide herd immunity. The uptake needs to be at least 70–80% to be effective, otherwise outbreaks of disease will occur and even epidemics may be started. Immunization is not without its problems but care with its use, avoidance in some children who have severe specific allergies, lead to safe programmes. Fears about the safety and unusual complications of the Measles, Mumps and Rubella vaccine (MMR), lack of clear medical information and advice, as well as misguided media publicity led to a serious fall-off in the rate of immunization. As a result there have been minor outbreaks of diseases due to lack of immunity. The general public needs to be given full and honest information as part of good medical ethics, so that they understand the needs of the whole community and the value of herd immunity.

'USING DOCTORS TO EXTRACT INFORMATION – IMPLICATING DOCTORS IN TORTURE'

Doctors have been used to inflict torture by medical means. The motivation for these actions may be the absence of a developed set of moral values or that pressure has been placed on individuals for monetary or political gain or in some cases the threat to their families. Many of the physical and psychological techniques used by governmental and terrorist organizations have been researched and developed by doctors who have clearly worked outside the accepted medical codes. Despite the Nuremberg Code of 1947, many regimes and agencies including those of western democracies continue to use techniques of torture to extract information. Some of the studies carried out exposing convicts to radiotherapy or other radiation in the USA without their express consent may be considered by some as a form of torture.

DISPOSAL OF THE BODY AND BODY PARTS

From the living

The surgical removal of tissues or organs for diagnostic or therapeutic purposes is carried out after due consent. Traditionally biopsy material was stored so that tissues could be re-examined at a later date if necessary. This tissue resource also provides material for research and development of new diagnostic procedures to refine and expand the information available on the diseased tissue. Following the Alder Hey Hospital (2003) revelations that whole organs from dead children had been kept without permission, new legislation (The Human Tissue Act 2004) was enacted regarding the removal and storage and use of organs. In the past, consent had been assumed at the time of surgery or post-mortem. Appropriate public education about the procedures especially from the Royal Colleges would have gone a long way to assuage the hurt, grief and rage felt by relatives of the deceased children. It has been common practice to preserve organs, which would demonstrate, congenital or disease abnormalities for the education of doctors and nurses. The ethical use of tissues and organs remains an important part of medical research and teaching. Most patients will consent to the use for these purposes and this consent can be obtained at the time of obtaining consent for the surgical procedure.

The Human Tissue Act 2004 has also been designed to regulate the use of organs from the living. Due to the shortage of cadaveric donor organs, there has been a huge expansion in living donor transplantation in the UK with over 600 being carried out in 2005. The donation of organs by the living will be overseen and audited by the Human Tissue Authority (HTA). Prospective donors of organs or parts of organs need to be fully informed of the procedures and risks of removing the organ for transplantation both immediate and in the long term. There should be no pressure on relatives to provide.

From the dead

With due consent one can remove organs from the deceased for preservation prior to transplantation. The Human Tissue Act 2004 has overhauled the procedures concerning organ donation. A working group of the Human Tissue Authority (HTA) was set up to implement the Act. The HTA has made it clear that if a deceased person consented to organ donation in life, then their organs can be removed without the need for the next of kin to sign a lack of objection or consent form. The public must be made aware of these changes and to become more involved in donating and recycling their organs. Currently the world's largest human cadaveric transplant programme is in China where the majority of organs are obtained from executed criminals. Many will argue that the consent given for use of their organs cannot be guaranteed as having been given of their free will. Organs require to be preserved in the interval between death and re-implantation. The preservation techniques initially consisted of simple washout of the organ followed by cooling. Newer techniques of improved preservation have been used to allow greater time to prepare the recipient. More recently perfusion of the donor organ is being used to prolong the interval between removal of the organ and transplantation. This permits transfer of organs across distances to the most appropriate recipient. It may also enhance the subsequent function of the graft and increase the number of patients who may benefit from transplantation. Human bodies are also used for anatomical dissection, surgical practice and development of imaging techniques. Use of bodies for these purposes requires consent or ideally donation by the incumbent during life.

TRANSPLANTATION

Organ replacement

The idea of organ or limb replacement is not new. Two Persian surgeons, St Cosmos and St Damian are credited with carrying out the first recorded replacement of a limb on a patient with a diseased leg (*c.* AD 300). This miracle is one of many which led to their sainthood after they were beheaded.[14] The first corneal graft was carried out by von Hippel in 1888.[15] Following the pioneering work of vascular anastomosis by Alexis Carrel in 1908, Lawler carried out the first human kidney transplant in 1950. However, successful organ transplantation was not a practical possibility until Roy Calne (later Prof. Sir Roy Calne, FRS), introduced chemotherapy for immunomodulation. The first successful functioning clinical graft was that of a kidney, at the Royal Free Hospital, by John Hopewell FRCS in November 1960. This was quickly followed over the next decade by heart and liver transplantation, which have now become routine. Ethical controversies concerning who should receive a replacement organ and which transplants are justified continue. The public and profession have a right to question the morality and cost to the entire transplant programme of repeated transplants in patients who fail to comply with medical advice to prevent damage to their newly transplanted organ.

Use of animal organs

Since it is unlikely that the supply of human organs will be sufficient to cover the demands of transplant surgery, researchers have looked at the possible use of animal organs from primates and pigs, so called 'xenotransplantation.' Heart valves from the pig have been implanted in the human heart since the 1960s.

Primate hearts have been unsuccessfully transplanted in humans. Pig livers have been successfully used to provide temporary liver support to patients while their own livers recovered function.[16] It is in this context that I first came to know Lord Jakobovits in 1969. He supported our work in using pig livers as temporary liver transplants in patients with liver failure.[17] In view of the concerns about the potential transfer of known and unknown viruses from animal organs, this xenograft research has largely been halted until we have some clarification of the ethical and infectious hazards that may be faced.

This essay has reviewed some of the most difficult issues facing patients, doctors and policy makers. These are issues concerning the quality of life, the rights to medical care and the autonomy of the individual. All have sharp ethical dilemmas attached to them. Perhaps the guiding principle should be that of 'doing the right thing.' This of course begs the question: what is the 'right thing?' It is this question which links the ethical debate of the public and philosophers with the practices of the medical profession. The four lectures in this volume attempt to address some of the issues generated by this question.

ACKNOWLEDGEMENTS

I am grateful to family and friends and especially John Carrier for their constructive criticism and suggestions.

NOTES

[1] Pelligrino, E.D. (2001) The internal morality of clinical medicine: a paradigm for the ethics of helping and healing professions, *J Med Philos* 26, 559–579.

[2] Mason, J.K. (2006) Ethical principles and ethical practice', Clinical Ethics 1, 3–6

[3] *W v Edgell* (1990) 1 ALL ER 835, CA.

[4] The Caldicott Committee (1997) *Report on the review of patient-identifiable information*. Department of Health UK.

[5] *Chester v Afshar* (2004) UKHL 41.

[6] *Re C* (1994) 1 ALL ER 819.

[7] *F (Mental Patient: Sterilisation) Re* (1990) 2AC I.

[8] Senate of Surgery of Great Britain and Ireland (1997). *The Surgeon's Duty of Care*. (London, Senate of Surgery of Great Britain and Ireland).

[9] Department of Health (2001). *Reference Guide to Consent for Examination or Treatment*. (London: Department of Health).

[10] Steinbrook, R. (2006) 'Imposing personal responsibility for health', *New England Journal of Medicine* 355, 753–6.

[11] Bishop, G. and Brodkey, A.C. (2006) 'Personal responsibility and physician responsibility – West Virginia's Medicaid Plan', *N Engl J Med* 355, 756–8.

[12] Jakobovits, I. (1959) *Jewish Medical Ethics* (Bloch Publishing Company, New York p. 184)

[13] Glover, J. (2006) 'Should the child live? Doctors, families and conflict', *Clinical Ethics* 1, 52–9.

[14] Rutkow, I.M. (1993) *Surgery. An Illustrated History* (St Louis, USA, Mosby), pp. 100–1.

[15] Ditto.

[16] Parbhoo, S. (1974) 'Temporary Hepatic Support in Scientific Foundations of Surgery'. In: Wells, C., Kyle, J. and Dunphy, J.E., (London, Heinemann), chap 19, pp. 563–565.

[17] Parbhoo, S., Kennedy, J., James, I.M., Chalstrey, L.J., Ajdukiewicz, A., Brock, P.J., Xanalatos, C., Sayer, P., Sherlock, S. (1971) 'Extracorporeal pig-liver perfusion in treatment of hepatic coma due to fulminant hepatitis', *Lancet* 1, 659–65.

APPENDICES

Hippocratic Oath (~350 BC)
Declaration of Geneva
The Nuremberg Code (1947) – permissible medical experiments
Declaration of Helsinki – World Medical Association 1964 revised in Edinburgh 2000
Duties of a doctor registered with the General Medical Council (GMC UK) 2006

HIPPOCRATIC OATH

The Original Version

I swear by Apollo the healer, by Aesculapius, by Health and all the powers of healing, and call to witness all the gods and goddesses that I may keep this Oath and Promise to the best of my ability and judgement.

I will pay the same respect to my master in the Science as to my parents and share my life with him and pay all my debts to him. I will regard his sons as my brothers and teach them the Science, if they desire to learn it, without fee or contract. I will hand on precepts, lectures and all other learning to my sons, to those of my master and to those pupils duly apprenticed and sworn, and to none other.

I will use my power to help the sick to the best of my ability and judgement; I will abstain from harming or wronging any man by it.

I will not give a fatal draught to anyone if I am asked, nor will I suggest any such thing. Neither will I give a woman means to procure an abortion.

I will be chaste and religious in my life and in my practice.

I will not cut, even for the stone, but I will leave such procedures to the practitioners of that craft.

Whenever I go into a house, I will go to help the sick and never with the intention of doing harm or injury. I will not abuse my position to indulge in sexual contacts with the bodies of women or of men, whether they be freemen or slaves.

Whatever I see or hear, professionally or privately, which ought not to be divulged, I will keep secret and tell no one.

If, therefore, I observe this Oath and do not violate it, may I prosper both in my life and in my profession, earning good repute among all men for my time. If I transgress and forswear this oath, may my lot be otherwise.

(Translated by J Chadwick and WN Mann, 1950.)

Modern Version

Upon graduation, many medical students take a modern version of the oath written in 1964 by Louis Lasagna, Academic Dean of the School of Medicine at Tufts University, USA.

I swear to fulfill, to the best of my ability and judgment, this covenant:

I will respect the hard-won scientific gains of those physicians in whose steps I walk, and gladly share such knowledge as is mine with those who are to follow.

I will apply, for the benefit of the sick, all measures [that] are required, avoiding those twin traps of overtreatment and therapeutic nihilism.

I will remember that there is art to medicine as well as science, and that warmth, sympathy, and understanding may outweigh the surgeon's knife or the chemist's drug.

I will not be ashamed to say 'I know not,' nor will I fail to call in my colleagues when the skills of another are needed for a patient's recovery.

I will respect the privacy of my patients, for their problems are not disclosed to me that the world may know. Most especially must I tread with care in matters of life and death. If it is given me to save a life, all thanks. But it may also be within my power to take a life; this awesome responsibility must be faced with great humbleness and awareness of my own frailty. Above all, I must not play at God.

I will remember that I do not treat a fever chart, a cancerous growth, but a sick human being, whose illness may affect the person's family and economic stability. My responsibility includes these related problems, if I am to care adequately for the sick.

I will prevent disease whenever I can, for prevention is preferable to cure.

I will remember that I remain a member of society, with special obligations to all my fellow human beings, those sound of mind and body as well as the infirm.If I do not violate this oath, may I enjoy life and art, respected while I live and remembered with affection thereafter. May I always act so as to preserve the finest traditions of my calling and may I long experience the joy of healing those who seek my help.

DECLARATION OF GENEVA

Adopted by the 2nd General Assembly of the World Medical Association, Geneva, Switzerland, September 1948; and amended by the 22nd World Medical Assembly, Sydney, Australia, August 1968; and the 35th World Medical Assembly, Venice, Italy, October 1983; and the 46th WMA General Assembly, Stockholm, Sweden, September 1994; and editorially revised at the 170th Council Session, Divonne-les-Bains, France, May 2005; and the 173rd Council Session, Divonne-les-Bains, France, May 2006.

AT THE TIME OF BEING ADMITTED AS A MEMBER OF THE MEDICAL PROFESSION:

I SOLEMNLY PLEDGE to consecrate my life to the service of humanity;

I WILL GIVE to my teachers the respect and gratitude that is their due;

I WILL PRACTISE my profession with conscience and dignity;

THE HEALTH OF MY PATIENT will be my first consideration;

I WILL RESPECT the secrets that are confided in me, even after the patient has died;

I WILL MAINTAIN by all the means in my power, the honour and the noble traditions of the medical profession;

MY COLLEAGUES will be my sisters and brothers;

I WILL NOT PERMIT considerations of age, disease or disability, creed, ethnic origin, gender, nationality, political affiliation, race, sexual orientation, social standing or any other factor to intervene between my duty and my patient;

I WILL MAINTAIN the utmost respect for human life;

I WILL NOT USE my medical knowledge to violate human rights and civil liberties, even under threat;

I MAKE THESE PROMISES solemnly, freely and upon my honour.

(20 May 2006)

www.wma.net (world medical association)

THE NUREMBERG CODE (1947)

Permissible Medical Experiments

The great weight of the evidence before us to effect that certain types of medical experiments on human beings, when kept within reasonably well-defined bounds, conform to the ethics of the medical profession generally. The protagonists of the practice of human experimentation justify their views on the basis that such experiments yield results for the good of society that are unprocurable by other methods or means of study. All agree, however, that certain basic principles must be observed in order to satisfy moral, ethical and legal concepts:

1. The voluntary consent of the human subject is absolutely essential. This means that the person involved should have legal capacity to give consent; should be so situated as to be able to exercise free power of choice, without the intervention of any element of force, fraud, deceit, duress, overreaching, or other ulterior form of constraint or coercion; and should have sufficient knowledge and comprehension of the elements of the subject matter involved as to enable him to make an understanding and enlightened decision. This latter element requires that before the acceptance of an affirmative decision by the experimental subject there should be made known to him the nature, duration, and purpose of the experiment; the method and means by which it is to be conducted; all inconveniences and hazards reasonably to be expected;

and the effects upon his health or person which may possibly come from his participation in the experiment.

The duty and responsibility for ascertaining the quality of the consent rests upon each individual who initiates, directs, or engages in the experiment. It is a personal duty and responsibility which may not be delegated to another with impunity.

2. The experiment should be such as to yield fruitful results for the good of society, unprocurable by other methods or means of study, and not random and unnecessary in nature.

3. The experiment should be so designed and based on the results of animal experimentation and a knowledge of the natural history of the disease or other problem under study that the anticipated results justify the performance of the experiment.

4. The experiment should be so conducted as to avoid all unnecessary physical and mental suffering and injury.

5. No experiment should be conducted where there is an a priori reason to believe that death or disabling injury will occur; except, perhaps, in those experiments where the experimental physicians also serve as subjects.

6. The degree of risk to be taken should never exceed that determined by the humanitarian importance of the problem to be solved by the experiment.

7. Proper preparations should be made and adequate facilities provided to protect the experimental subject against even remote possibilities of injury, disability or death.

8. The experiment should be conducted only by scientifically qualified persons. The highest degree of skill and care should be required through all stages of the experiment of those who conduct or engage in the experiment.

9. During the course of the experiment the human subject should be at liberty to bring the experiment to an end if he has reached the physical or mental state where continuation of the experiment seems to him to be impossible.

10. During the course of the experiment the scientist in charge must be prepared to terminate the experiment at any stage, if he has probable cause to believe, in the exercise of the good faith, superior skill and careful judgment required of him, that a continuation of the experiment is likely to result in injury, disability, or death to the experimental subject.

(The Nuremberg Code (1947). In: Mitscherlich, A., Mielke, F. *Doctors of infamy: the story of the Nazi medical crimes*. (New York, Schuman, 1949), xxiii-xxv).

WORLD MEDICAL ASSOCIATION DECLARATION OF HELSINKI

Ethical Principles for Medical Research Involving Human Subjects

Adopted by the 18th WMA General Assembly, Helsinki, Finland, June 1964, and amended by the:

29th WMA General Assembly, Tokyo, Japan, October 1975
35th WMA General Assembly, Venice, Italy, October 1983
41st WMA General Assembly, Hong Kong, September 1989
48th WMA General Assembly, Somerset West, Republic of South Africa, October 1996 and the 52nd WMA General Assembly, Edinburgh, Scotland, October 2000
Note of Clarification on Paragraph 29 added by the WMA General Assembly, Washington 2002
Note of Clarification on Paragraph 30 added by the WMA General Assembly, Tokyo 2004

A. INTRODUCTION

1. The World Medical Association has developed the Declaration of Helsinki as a statement of ethical principles to provide guidance to physicians and other participants in medical research involving human subjects. Medical research involving human subjects includes research on identifiable human material or identifiable data.

2. It is the duty of the physician to promote and safeguard the health of the people. The physician's knowledge and conscience are dedicated to the fulfillment of this duty.

3. The Declaration of Geneva of the World Medical Association binds the physician with the words, 'The health of my patient will be my first consideration,' and the International Code of Medical Ethics declares that, 'A physician shall act only in the patient's interest when providing medical care which might have the effect of weakening the physical and mental condition of the patient.'

4. Medical progress is based on research which ultimately must rest in part on experimentation involving human subjects.

5. In medical research on human subjects, considerations related to the well-being of the human subject should take precedence over the interests of science and society.

6. The primary purpose of medical research involving human subjects is to improve prophylactic, diagnostic and therapeutic procedures and the understanding of the aetiology and pathogenesis of disease. Even the best proven prophylactic, diagnostic, and therapeutic methods must continuously be challenged through research for their effectiveness, efficiency, accessibility and quality.

7. In current medical practice and in medical research, most prophylactic, diagnostic and therapeutic procedures involve risks and burdens.

8   Medical research is subject to ethical standards that promote respect for all human beings and protect their health and rights. Some research populations are vulnerable and need special protection. The particular needs of the economically and medically disadvantaged must be recognized. Special attention is also required for those who cannot give or refuse consent for themselves, for those who may be subject to giving consent under duress, for those who will not benefit personally from the research and for those for whom the research is combined with care.

9   Research Investigators should be aware of the ethical, legal and regulatory requirements for research on human subjects in their own countries as well as applicable international requirements. No national ethical, legal or regulatory requirement should be allowed to reduce or eliminate any of the protections for human subjects set forth in this Declaration.

B. BASIC PRINCIPLES FOR ALL MEDICAL RESEARCH

10. It is the duty of the physician in medical research to protect the life, health, privacy, and dignity of the human subject.

11. Medical research involving human subjects must conform to generally accepted scientific principles, be based on a thorough knowledge of the scientific literature, other relevant sources of information, and on adequate laboratory and, where appropriate, animal experimentation.

12. Appropriate caution must be exercised in the conduct of research which may affect the environment, and the welfare of animals used for research must be respected.

13. The design and performance of each experimental procedure involving human subjects should be clearly formulated in an experimental protocol. This protocol should be submitted for consideration, comment, guidance, and where appropriate, approval to a specially appointed ethical review committee, which must be independent of the investigator, the sponsor or any other kind of undue influence. This independent committee should be in conformity with the laws and regulations of the country in which the research experiment is performed. The committee has the right to monitor ongoing trials. The researcher has the obligation to provide monitoring information to the committee, especially any serious adverse events. The researcher should also submit to the committee, for review, information regarding funding, sponsors, institutional affiliations, other potential conflicts of interest and incentives for subjects.

14. The research protocol should always contain a statement of the ethical considerations involved and should indicate that there is compliance with the principles enunciated in this Declaration.

15. Medical research involving human subjects should be conducted only by scientifically qualified persons and under the supervision of a clinically competent medical person. The responsibility for the human subject must always rest with a medically qualified person and never rest on the subject of the research, even though the subject has given consent.

16. Every medical research project involving human subjects should be preceded by careful assessment of predictable risks and burdens in comparison with foreseeable benefits to the subject or to others. This does not preclude the participation of healthy volunteers in medical research. The design of all studies should be publicly available.

17. Physicians should abstain from engaging in research projects involving human subjects unless they are confident that the risks involved have been adequately assessed and can be satisfactorily managed. Physicians should cease any investigation if the risks are found to outweigh the potential benefits or if there is conclusive proof of positive and beneficial results.

18. Medical research involving human subjects should only be conducted if the importance of the objective outweighs the inherent risks and burdens to the subject. This is especially important when the human subjects are healthy volunteers.

19. Medical research is only justified if there is a reasonable likelihood that the populations in which the research is carried out stand to benefit from the results of the research.

20. The subjects must be volunteers and informed participants in the research project.

21. The right of research subjects to safeguard their integrity must always be respected. Every precaution should be taken to respect the privacy of the subject, the confidentiality of the patient's information and to minimize the impact of the study on the subject's physical and mental integrity and on the personality of the subject.

22. In any research on human beings, each potential subject must be adequately informed of the aims, methods, sources of funding, any possible conflicts of interest, institutional affiliations of the researcher, the anticipated benefits and potential risks of the study and the discomfort it may entail. The subject should be informed of the right to abstain from participation in the study or to withdraw consent to participate at any time without reprisal. After ensuring that the subject has understood the information, the physician should then obtain the subject's freely-given informed consent, preferably in writing. If the consent cannot be obtained in writing, the non-written consent must be formally documented and witnessed.

23. When obtaining informed consent for the research project the physician should be particularly cautious if the subject is in a dependent relationship with the physician or may consent under duress. In that case the informed consent should be obtained by a well-informed physician who is not engaged in the investigation and who is completely independent of this relationship.

24. For a research subject who is legally incompetent, physically or mentally incapable of giving consent or is a legally incompetent minor, the investigator must obtain informed consent from the legally authorized representative in accordance with applicable law. These groups should not be included in research unless the research is necessary to promote

the health of the population represented and this research cannot instead be performed on legally competent persons.

25. When a subject deemed legally incompetent, such as a minor child, is able to give assent to decisions about participation in research, the investigator must obtain that assent in addition to the consent of the legally authorized representative.

26. Research on individuals from whom it is not possible to obtain consent, including proxy or advance consent, should be done only if the physical/mental condition that prevents obtaining informed consent is a necessary characteristic of the research population. The specific reasons for involving research subjects with a condition that renders them unable to give informed consent should be stated in the experimental protocol for consideration and approval of the review committee. The protocol should state that consent to remain in the research should be obtained as soon as possible from the individual or a legally authorized surrogate.

27. Both authors and publishers have ethical obligations. In publication of the results of research, the investigators are obliged to preserve the accuracy of the results. Negative as well as positive results should be published or otherwise publicly available. Sources of funding, institutional affiliations and any possible conflicts of interest should be declared in the publication. Reports of experimentation not in accordance with the principles laid down in this Declaration should not be accepted for publication.

C. ADDITIONAL PRINCIPLES FOR MEDICAL RESEARCH COMBINED WITH MEDICAL CARE

28. The physician may combine medical research with medical care, only to the extent that the research is justified by its potential prophylactic, diagnostic or therapeutic value. When medical research is combined with medical care, additional standards apply to protect the patients who are research subjects.

29. The benefits, risks, burdens and effectiveness of a new method should be tested against those of the best current prophylactic, diagnostic, and therapeutic methods. This does not exclude the use of placebo, or no treatment, in studies where no proven prophylactic, diagnostic or therapeutic method exists.

30. At the conclusion of the study, every patient entered into the study should be assured of access to the best proven prophylactic, diagnostic and therapeutic methods identified by the study.

31. The physician should fully inform the patient which aspects of the care are related to the research. The refusal of a patient to participate in a study must never interfere with the patient-physician relationship.

32. In the treatment of a patient, where proven prophylactic, diagnostic and therapeutic methods do not exist or have been ineffective, the physician, with informed consent from the patient, must be free to use unproven or new prophylactic, diagnostic and therapeutic measures, if in the

physician's judgement it offers hope of saving life, re-establishing health or alleviating suffering. Where possible, these measures should be made the object of research, designed to evaluate their safety and efficacy. In all cases, new information should be recorded and, where appropriate, published. The other relevant guidelines of this Declaration should be followed.

[1] Note of clarification on paragraph 29 of the WMA Declaration of Helsinki:

The WMA hereby reaffirms its position that extreme care must be taken in making use of a placebo-controlled trial and that in general this methodology should only be used in the absence of existing proven therapy. However, a placebo-controlled trial may be ethically acceptable, even if proven therapy is available, under the following circumstances:

> Where for compelling and scientifically sound methodological reasons its use is necessary to determine the efficacy or safety of a prophylactic, diagnostic or therapeutic method; or
> Where a prophylactic, diagnostic or therapeutic method is being investigated for a minor condition and the patients who receive placebo will not be subject to any additional risk of serious or irreversible harm.

All other provisions of the Declaration of Helsinki must be adhered to, especially the need for appropriate ethical and scientific review.

[2] Note of clarification on paragraph 30 of the WMA Declaration of Helsinki

The WMA hereby reaffirms its position that it is necessary during the study planning process to identify post-trial access by study participants to prophylactic, diagnostic and therapeutic procedures identified as beneficial in the study or access to other appropriate care. Post-trial access arrangements or other care must be described in the study protocol so the ethical review committee may consider such arrangements during its review. (9 October 2004)

DUTIES OF A DOCTOR REGISTERED WITH THE GENERAL MEDICAL COUNCIL (GMC UK) 2006

Patients must be able to trust doctors with their lives and wellbeing. To justify that trust, we as a profession have duty to maintain a good standard of practice and care and to show respect for human life. In particular as a doctor you must:

● make the care of your patient your first concern;
● treat every patient politely and considerately;
● respect patients' dignity and privacy;
● listen to patients and respect their views;
● give patients information in a way they can understand;

- respect the rights of patients to be fully involved in decisions about their care;
- keep your professional knowledge and skills up to date;
- recognise the limits of your professional competence;
- to be honest and trustworthy;
- respect and protect confidential information;
- make sure that your personal beliefs do not prejudice your patients' care;
- act quickly to protect patients from risk if you have good reason to believe that you or a colleague may not be fit to practice;
- avoid abusing your position as a doctor; and
- work with colleagues in the ways that best serve patients' interests.

In all these matters you must never discriminate unfairly against your patients or colleagues. And you must always be prepared to justify your actions to them.

Good Medical Practice (GMC, 2001)

LORD JAKOBOVITS: A PERSONAL APPRECIATION

Yoel (Julian) Jakobovits MD*

The editors of this exceptionally fine volume graced by some of Britain's finest thinkers have asked that I provide a Foreword, written from a personal perspective. When testimony rests on facts, and when these are of public record, even one with strong emotional links may be a reliable source. As a son, I am of course not expected to be altogether impartial. I write not as an evaluator nor judge but merely as an observer, albeit a biased one, presenting the record as I have been especially privileged to see it. On the other hand, the reader might find some special worth in my presentation, allowing strictly legal disabilities to be outweighed by the advantages of intimacy and familiarity which I can claim over any other less partial attestants.

In addition to some personal and biographical vignettes, I have outlined the ways in which my father aided in developing the field of Jewish medical ethics, from its earliest days to the widely recognized and much discussed area of study and wider interest it has become today.

My father was born in Koenigsberg, Germany – now Kaliningrad after its annexation by Russia on 8 February 1921. His father was Dayan Dr Julius Jakobovits who was then serving as the Orthodox rabbi of Koenigsberg. Schooled in the Hungarian *yeshivot* (rabbinic academies), my grandfather was also a great admirer of Immanuel Kant. In fact, although my father's Hebrew name was *Yisrael*, after a great uncle, he was civilly named in honour of the great philosopher – whose name also began with an 'I' and ended with an 'l'.

My paternal grandfather hailed from a family of eight, six brothers and two sisters. Of the men, three became rabbis and three became physicians. Of

* Dr Yoel (Julian) Jakobovits was born in Dublin, Ireland, in 1950. He moved at age 8 to New York. The eldest of six children, he lived in midtown Manhattan, and attended yeshiva day schools throughout elementary and high school years. He transferred to Ner Israel Rabbinical College in Baltimore in 1967 and studied at Johns Hopkins University, majoring in chemistry.

In 1971 he rejoined his parents – his late father was then appointed Chief Rabbi of the United Hebrew Congregations of Great Britain and the Commonwealth – to pursue his medical studies at the University of London. In 1973 he married Michelle Tauber of New York. After qualification in 1976, Dr Jakobovits returned to the United States to take his residency training at Maimonides Medical Center in Brooklyn, New York. In 1980, he moved back to Baltimore for Fellowship training at Johns Hopkins in gastroenterology.

Since 1982 Dr Jakobovits has been on the staff of Sinai Hospital in Baltimore and holds an appointment as Assistant Professor of Medicine at The Johns Hopkins University School of Medicine. At Sinai Hospital he is an Attending Physician in the Division of General Medicine and the Division of Gastroenterology. He maintains a busy private and teaching practice.

Dr Jakobovits, his wife and family live on the campus of the Ner Israel Rabbinical College, Baltimore. There he is the resident physician for over 2000 people who now live in the College grounds.

the women, one married a rabbi and the other married a physician. With this strikingly even distribution in the genes, it is not surprising that my father intertwined the two traditions, rabbinic and medical. Of course, the alliance of rabbinics and medicine is nothing new; many leading medieval sages earned their way in this world by practising medicine and in the next world by practising rabbinics.

Fearing the rising Nazi menace, my grandfather arranged through the help of Rabbi Dr Solomon Schonfeld, who saved so many lives, for his eldest son, my father, to escape to England. He arrived in London late in 1936, at the age of 16 and two years before the rest of the family joined him there. My father entered the Yeshiva Etz Chaim and concurrently obtained ministerial training at Jew's College. Actually, he had at first registered as a student at Queen's College, London, intending to undertake a career in mathematics. However, my grandfather, insisted that as his eldest son he follow in the family tradition of rabbinics.

The critical role which my mother played in my father's evolving career cannot be overstated. She more than anyone inspired him to harness his great intellectual gifts in the service of the community at large. Were it not for my mother, my father might well have remained for all his days, a relatively unknown iconoclastic researcher in Dublin where he arrived in 1949 as Chief Rabbi. My mother, with her tremendous sense of values and *joie de vivre* continues to inspire many in the family and beyond with his message and mission.

Ireland is, of course, a strictly Roman Catholic country. It was estimated that during those years 97% of the population were Roman Catholics, 3% were Protestants, and the Jews – constituting a fraction of a per cent. The widespread public influence of the Church and its teachings prompted examination of practically all issues through the prism of religion. The Church had a ready answer for virtually every question, and as Chief Rabbi, my father was frequently consulted regarding the parallel Jewish opinion. As questions arose, the immense mass of original sources had to be consulted again and again in order to clarify the authentic Jewish attitudes. By contrast, the Catholic community had many easily available books that collected their teachings on medico-moral matters. Thus, medical ethics from the Jewish perspective became my father's primary interest for rabbinic, and academic, reasons. In a predominantly Roman Catholic country he hoped to position Jewish medical ethics prominently on the medical map, academic map and rabbinic map.

As Chief Rabbi of Ireland, my father felt it only proper to obtain his doctorate from an Irish university. To this end he approached Trinity College, Dublin. The faculty at Trinity decided not to accept his candidature because of the invidious position they would be in were they to reject the country's Chief Rabbi's dissertation! More seriously, Trinity could provide neither scholars as competent referees nor as adequate literary resources in this still-nascent discipline. Consequently, he had to turn to the University of London and made many a trip across the Irish Sea to consult that institution's vast literary holdings. Moreover, London could provide qualified mentors, though it took three who between them had the necessary credentials. The three were: Rabbi Dr Isidore Epstein, Principal of Jew's College, chosen for his rabbinic scholarship; Professor Charles Singer, son of Singer of *Singer's Prayer Book* fame, who was the leading general medical historian of his day in England; and Dr. Siegfried Stein, a widely recognized expert on medieval Hebrew literature. The Wellcome Historical Medical Library, the collections at Jew's College and The British Museum, in London, in addition to those at the Bibliothèque Nationale in Paris and Trinity College in Dublin, provided abundant and indispensable literary resources. Years later, the Wellcome's location across the street from Adler House, the seat of the British Chief Rabbinate at that time, prompted my father to say that the story of his rabbinic career stretches across the width of the intervening street!

The thesis was first submitted to the University of London in 1955 and was subsequently published in 1959. In 1966 a Hebrew edition appeared entitled *haRefuah v'Hayahadus* and in 1975 a forty-page chapter on recent developments was added. The first edition contains a Foreword by my late maternal grandfather, Rabbi Dr Elie Munk of Paris. Alas, my paternal grandfather died in 1947 and though he had a profound influence on my father, he was not spared to see my father's literary or other rabbinic achievements. On the other hand, my maternal grandfather lived until 1983 and provided guidance and encouragement over many years. In his Foreword, my grandfather underscores several critical points that retain their truth concerning this book specifically and my father's overall outlook more generally. In particular, he refers to the book's intellectual and sensitive treatment of :

> "The vast subjects of medico-moral conflict ... which have not ceased, over the generations, to beset the moral conscience of humanity."

The book's title, *Jewish Medical Ethics*, has been universally adopted as the designation of the specialty to which it gave birth. An argument can be made that the term *law* should have been used in place of *ethics*. After all, it is hard even to find an exact Hebrew equivalent of the term *ethics*. Arguably, there are no distinct Jewish ethics as these are incorporated wholly within the rubric of Jewish law, *halakha*. Comprising civil and ritual law, morals, and ethics, the *halakha* does not recognize any substantial difference between these categories and legislates for each in conjunction with the others.

Nevertheless, the concept of 'ethics' in *Jewish Medical Ethics* is pivotal. I believe that the use of this term rather than '*halakha*', or even 'law,' has contributed significantly to the development of Jewish medical ethics as a recognized autonomous academic discipline. By employing terminology akin to that which describes the prevailing discipline of general medical ethics, many who are more secularly inclined have also come to regard the Jewish enterprise with similar seriousness. Consequently, the subject grew immensely since the seeds were first planted by *Jewish Medical Ethics*, in parallel with the now widely-accepted programmes of secular medical ethics.

Continuing evolution is evidenced by the burgeoning literature, including books and periodicals in several languages, by the establishment of university chairs, and by regular international meetings. All of this may have been impeded, if the languages of academia and that of Judaic scholarship were to have been fundamentally strange to one another. The term ethics, though perhaps not entirely correct in the Jewish context, is the single crucial term which has made these parallel developments possible by bridging the *halakhic* world with its wider counterpart.

Of note, my father never attempted to erect the bridge in the other direction, to bring secular ethical concepts into the language of Jewish conceptualization. Currently popular terms such as autonomy, beneficence, non-maleficence, or distributive justice[1] never figure in his writings or speeches.

My father's penchant for focussing Jewish teachings on the complexities of modern life was evident throughout his career, beyond the confines of medical *halakha*.

His chief focus was to proclaim Jewish values in contemporary language and current frames of reference in ways that are convincing and attractive to modern men and women, whether committed to Jewish practice or not. In this respect he did not distinguish between Orthodox and non-Orthodox. He frequently stressed his dislike of the term Orthodox altogether claiming that there is only one body of Jewish law. Furthermore, a recurrent theme in his *Weltanschauung* stressed the overarching obligation to project Jewish teachings in a way that attracts the attention and respect of society at large. The application of many medical *halakhic* principles should be seen in their universal context as well as in their more confined Jewish sphere. As one of his critics writes: 'It may be that Immanuel Jakobovits was the first to begin to systematically address the varied and challenging elements of Jewish medical ethics in a way intended for both scholar and lay-person, for both Jew and Gentile. Every Jewish scholar of medical ethics will be eternally in his debt for his pioneering work.'[2]

In summary, *Jewish Medical Ethics* is unique and pioneering in three fundamental respects. It was the first book to review and organize the diverse sources and opinions regarding Jewish views of medical practice. Secondly, it was written in English. And finally, it repeatedly stresses the ethical dimensions embedded in these rulings. These latter two features are combined to project a general ethical view which often speaks beyond the Jewish community in universal tones as well. This volume of essays may be seen as a further contribution to the relationship between ethics and law as applied to medical practice.

In 1958 my father accepted a call to become the first rabbi of the newly founded Fifth Avenue Synagogue of New York. In sharp contrast with Ireland, this brought him to the very heart of one of the world's largest Jewish communities. In addition, New York was home to many Orthodox Jewish physicians and scientists, and Jewish hospitals. This stimulating environment provided my father with many opportunities to further develop the still fledgling field of Jewish medical ethics.

During this period he continued to lecture widely, locally and throughout the country. Among my warmest childhood memories are those special evenings when I would accompany him to a lecture within driving distance from home. I still recall how invigorating he found these interchanges, especially the question and answer periods which followed the main presentation. I remember being struck by the broad similarity in the questions among the varied audiences.

I also recall that many medical ethics lectures in those days began with a plea that ethical decision-making in medicine be seen as a discrete and necessary subspeciality. Just as a non-specialist physician would turn to a specialist cardiologist or neurologist for help with a difficult cardiac or neurologic problem, physicians ought to seek help from ethics specialists when faced with moral dilemmas. Frequently, these arguments prompted vigorous resistance by doctors who regarded their professional training and experience as license to pronounce on the ethical as well as technical nature of their ministrations. These attitudes reflected the generally unchallenged paternalistic posture of doctors in those days. A measure of the enormous change which has occurred in this regard is indicated by the currently widespread acceptance of ethics programmes, and even ethics departments, in medical schools and university medical centres as compared with the entire absence of, nay resistance to, 'outside' expertise in those early days.

The Fifth Avenue Synagogue provided a venue for my father to develop important medical relationships over many years. During these years he conducted a twice-weekly *shiur* (class) attended by dozens of physicians, nurses, and allied medical personnel. This *shiur* had a reincarnation in later years in London, where my father met every month or two with about twenty doctors and allied professionals. The purpose of these encounters was to support dual-directional flow of information. My father gained updated information about current medical advances and problems while the audience gained by hearing authentically Jewish insights and evaluations directly related to their practices.

The cross-fertilization of ideas and concepts bore numerous fruits. One was the development, for the first time, of a practical guide for Jewish doctors and the institutions in which they work (*A Hospital Compendium: a guide to Jewish moral and religious principles in hospital practice*, New York, Commission on Synagogue Relations (1963), 28 pp. (Co-editor). Reprinted under the Title 'Medicine and religion – the Jewish view', *Nu Sigma Nu*, 48 (Wisconsin 1963) pp. 48–56). The guide was designed to help doctors deal with the ritual and the medical ethical problems arising in the care of observant Jewish patients. By now, over 100,000 copies of the *Hospital Compendium* – now its sixth edition – have been distributed. It continues to serve as a model of the application of traditional sources to modern medical perplexities. Similarly, the committee in which my father brought together rabbis, attorneys, physicians, and philosophers remains a paragon of interdisciplinary approaches to vexing societal difficulties

My father devoted many articles to clarifying the *halakhic* attitude to contraception, population control, and the problems of abortion. As in the case of autopsies, he frequently stressed the wider social implications of *halakhic* guidelines in addition to the more narrowly-focused legal aspects. He often argued that the ready availability of contraceptive and abortion services gave birth to the age of 'credit-card morality,' enabling people to 'enjoy now and pay later'.

Since the appearance of *Jewish Medical Ethics* several developments confirm the remarkable maturation of Jewish medical ethics over the ensuing five decades. First, there has been a veritable explosion in secondary texts devoted to Jewish medical ethics written in the current vernacular. There has also been an enormous increase in periodical literature. Leading speciality rabbinic and communal journals in the United States and abroad almost always include some medically-related article in each issue. This growth is reflected in the striking fact that while the original *Jewish Encyclopedia* (1901–6) had not a single entry devoted to medical ethics, the current *Encyclopedia Judaica* (1972) has over a dozen, many of them contributed by my father (for example: *Encyclopedia Judaica* – articles: 'Artificial insemination', vol. 3 cols 660–1; 'Birth control', vol. 4 cols 1053–4; 'Castration', vol. 5 cols 242–3; 'Celibacy', vol. 5 cols 268–9; 'Euthanasia', vol. 6 cols 978–9; 'Sex', vol. 14 cols 1206–7, Jerusalem, *Encyclopedia Judaica*, 1971).

The plethora of books and journals has been crowned by the establishment, mainly in Israel, of independent and university-based centres for the study of Jewish medical ethics. Chief in the latter category is the Jakobovits Center for the Study of Jewish Medical Ethics at Ben Gurion Medical Center in Beersheba and the Falk Schlesinger Institute at the Shaare Zedek Hospital in Jerusalem. In addition to confirming the expansion and recognition of the speciality as an academic discipline, these developments point to the broadening acceptance of the guiding role which religiously-based ethical analysis can provide for those who would submit to its values and guidelines. Such institutes are now also attached to the Albert Einstein College of Medicine in New York and Jew's College in London. Shortly after my father's demise, Bar Ilan University launched plans to build a new centre, in my father's memory, devoted to law, ethics, and medicine. This magnificent centre was dedicated in Tel Aviv in June 2006.

My father firmly believed that the rabbi's role is not inventive. It is, above all, interpretive. It is this quality which was cited by Viscount Tonypandy, former Speaker of the House of Commons, when he nominated my father for the 1991 Templeton Foundation's award for progress in religion. Awarded annually since 1973, the Prize endeavours to grant outstanding religious and spiritual contributions status comparable with the recognition of the Nobel Prizes for other prominent contributions to civilization. My Father was the first Jewish recipient. Other previous holders of this award included Mother Teresa (1973) and Alexander Solzhenitsyn (1983). This is what Viscount Tonypandy said:

> The Chief Rabbi's contribution to medical ethics is unique and remains pre-eminent. Among his extensive writings are classic expositions of Jewish law of unsurpassed knowledge and enlightened humanity.

In exercising rabbinic leadership, my father never shied away from controversial issues and has occasionally championed unpopular views. For example, reference *The Times* of London (9 November 1987) and his speech in the House of Lords in a debate on the obligations of citizenship (Hansard, Her Majesty's Printing Office, London, 8 December 1993, columns 968–970.

In conclusion, I have tried to present a personal, yet hopefully, an accurate sketch of my father's singular contributions to Jewish medical ethics. I have emphasized the courageous way in which he presented Jewish moral teachings, true to authentic sources on the one hand and in contemporary terms on the other. It can be said without exaggeration, that in addition to being my biological father, he is the undisputed father of Jewish medical ethics.

My father was blessed with a remarkably active and meaningful life until the very end. On the last *shabbat* of his life, he attended all the services, as usual. After *shabbat,* upon returning home, he recited the *havdalah* prayer. Not feeling well, he lay down. He took with him a *chumash*, a Hebrew bible, intending to prepare comments to make the next day when he was due to lead a rabbinic delegation in the hope of enlisting the help of the President of France in relieving the plight of thirteen Jews held prisoner in Iran. Occupied with this *mitzva*, his condition rapidly deteriorated as he returned his soul to its Maker.

Yoel Jakobovits MD

NOTE

1 Beauchamp T.L., Childress J.F. Principles of Biomedical Ethics, 5th Ed. Oxford 5001 (OUP).
2 Gelman, M.A. (1993) 'On Immanuel Jakobovits: Bringing the Ancient Word to the Modern World' In: Allen Verhey, Stephen E. Lammas (eds) *Theological Voices in Medical Ethics* (Wm. B. Eerdmans Publishing, Grand Rapids, Michigan).

CANCERKIN AND THE
JAKOBOVITS CONNECTION

Gloria Freilich, Co-founder and Chief Executive, Cancerkin

Cancerkin, the first hospital-based breast cancer charity in the UK, was founded in 1987, at a time when there was very little information about the disease available to the general public and the word 'cancer' was usually only mentioned in metaphors. The UK National Breast Screening Programme had yet to be launched and the concepts of support and rehabilitation services for patient and family members and advice for high risk families had yet to be developed in the UK. In this context and initially operating from a small room in the Royal Free Hospital, Cancerkin began to develop its comprehensive programme of treatment, supportive care, rehabilitation, education and research. In so doing, it has pioneered a dynamic example of collaboration between the voluntary sector and the National Health Service in the field of breast cancer and its achievements have attracted national and international endorsement as a desirable healthcare model.

'Treat the patient, not just the cancer' has always been Cancerkin's maxim. Its patient support programmes help people cope better with their disease and the effects of its treatment. Patients and relatives can make immediate contact and receive accurate information, individual or group psychological and emotional support and can benefit from a wide range of rehabilitation programmes, when they need them most.

The charity also supports and is involved in research. Over the years projects have included: research into the role of scintimammography in breast imaging, robotic recognition and assessment of mammographic abnormalities, aromatase activity in the breast and breast cancer, angiogenesis in breast cancer, the influence of hormone replacement therapy on the development of breast cancer, the development of lymphoedema and its response to various conventional and new therapies, as well as the influence of obesity on the development and persistence of lymphoedema and on the efficacy of its treatment.

The charity is also involved in the provision of education for health professionals, medical students and the volunteers who play an important part in its work. Cancerkin has played a leading role in pioneering the breast cancer patient advocacy movement throughout Europe, through the establishment of Europa Donna, the European Breast Cancer Coalition.

Today, Cancerkin as the London regional breast cancer charity, operates from the purpose-built Cancerkin Centre on site at its home hospital, the Royal Free. It currently also cares for patients referred from 35 hospitals throughout London and surrounding areas. All patient and family services are available free of charge, regardless of where patients receive their breast cancer treatment, yet Cancerkin does not benefit from NHS funding and is dependent entirely on voluntary support. The scope of Cancerkin's programmes can be seen on www.cancerkin.org.uk

None of this work would be possible without the countless individuals, companies and charitable trusts, whose support and involvement over the years has been constant and generous and it is here that the story of the Jakobovits connection began.

Early in 1987, together with the late Philip Mishon OBE, the charity's first Fundraising Chairman, I visited Lord and Lady Jakobovits, for the purpose of introducing them to our plans for the development of this fledgling, secular charity, as its base was so close to their home. We were warmly received and Lady Jakobovits' immediate reaction was to volunteer her services to offer emotional support to patients and family members. Among Cancerkin's multi-faith constituency there is a considerable proportion of Jewish patients for whom a visit from 'Lady J', as she is fondly and universally known was, and still is, a tonic and a blessing. We were later joined by Lord Jakobovits and as we continued to discuss the charity's plans our hosts, with all their characteristic warmth and generosity, offered to open their home for a fundraising dinner. Lady J immediately rallied her friends and contacts and just three months later, our cause was introduced to a guest list of leading medical specialists and philanthropists whose contributions on that evening alone funded the development of Cancerkin's early programmes. Moreover, many of those present have remained great friends and supporters of the cause to this day.

Three hectic years of development ensued as Cancerkin grew rapidly in response to patient and family need. It soon became clear, however, that operating from one 'grace and favour' room within the Royal Free Hospital had become an impossible limitation. We had to consider expansion. In 1990, an appeal was launched to raise £1 million needed to build a dedicated Cancerkin Centre.

A few months later, Lord Jakobovits retired as Chief Rabbi of the United Hebrew Congregations of Great Britain and the Commonwealth and we decided to mark the event. In gratitude for Lord and Lady Jakobovits' unfailing patronage, a Gala Dinner chaired by the late Lord Goodman, was organized at London's Guildhall. In the course of the evening tributes were offered by distinguished philanthropic, medical and political personalities, all graciously acknowledged by Lady Jakobovits on behalf of her husband and herself. It was unanimously agreed that the proceeds of the Guildhall Dinner should fund the building and equipping of the Lady J Clinic in the new Cancerkin Centre, for the treatment of lymphoedema in breast cancer patients.

The Lady J Clinic was formally dedicated at the Cancerkin Centre's Opening Ceremony on 10th October 1994. Working beyond the scope of the

National Health Service, it is renowned for providing treatment using Combined Decongestive Therapy for this debilitating and distressing condition, along the lines practised in leading lymphoedema centres in continental Europe.

In 1999, news of the death of Lord Jakobovits was received with the greatest sorrow and regret. The qualities of his intellectual rigour, holiness, nobility and humanity are seldom combined in one person and they made his contribution to society always stimulating and quite unique.

How Cancerkin would choose to commemorate him was not a difficult decision and one which I broached with Lady Jakobovits in the months following the period of mourning. A series of lectures in which each of the speakers and their chosen topics would be selected to reflect Lord Jakobovits' deep and abiding interest and expertise in medical ethics, was felt to be entirely appropriate. With Lady Jakobovits' advice, we are confident that he would have appreciated the lectures and their publication, not merely as a tribute, for he was a modest man. Instead, he would have viewed them as sources of enlightenment for the benefit of those who seek to care for humanity at large.

The Cancerkin Centre
Royal Free Hospital
London
www.cancerkin.org.uk

107

THE LECTURE COMMITTEE

Cancerkin is grateful to members of the committee for their kind assistance and support in organizing the lecture series and to the publication group (*) for their work in preparing this volume:

*John Carrier PhD (Chairman)

Recently Dean of Graduate Studies, The London School of Economics and Political Science; Chair of the Royal Free Hampstead NHS Trust 1997–2001; Chair of Camden Primary Care Trust 2001–present.

Dr Joseph S. Adler

Dr Adler graduated from King's College Hospital Medical School in 1981. Subsequently he undertook postgraduate training at Maimonides Hospital in New York, returning to become a principal in General Practice in North West London in 1988. He worked as a clinical assistant in cardiology at the Royal Free Hospital. He is a son-in-law of the late Lord Jakobovits and has a special interest in the ethics of medical practice.

Dr Simon L. Cohen MB, BS, MRCP, FRCP

Dr Cohen is Consultant Physician and Nephrologist, Intensive Care Unit, University College London Hospitals. Lecturer in Medicine, UCL Medical School. Overseas appointments have included Chicago Medical School, University of Minnesota Medical School and Beilinson Hospital Renal Transplant Unit, Israel.

Author of 80 peer review paper, Dr Cohen is also sole author of *Whose Life is it Anyhow* (Robson Books).

His major research interests are in ethics and nephrology. Principal activities have included co-chairmanship of the Working Party on Ethics of the European Society of Intensive Care Medicine (1994–8), Co-ordinator ETHICUS Project of the European Union – looking at withholding and withdrawing treatment in the intensive care unit (1998–2001), UK Co-ordinator of ETHICATT EU project on ethical attitudes in ICU (2000–3).

Dr Cohen also serves as a regular expert witness in medico legal matters and as an examiner at the University of London.

*Gloria Freilich

Co-founder (1987) and Chief Executive of the London regional breast cancer charity Cancerkin; introduced and developed information, support and rehabilitation programmes for patients and their families.

From 1990–4, she served on the UICC Reach to Recovery International Committee (Geneva) with special responsibility for researching and promoting development of breast cancer peer support services and patient advocacy in Latin America.

In 1992, Gloria Freilich introduced the American 'Look Good ... Feel Better' programme to the UK. Launched at the Cancerkin Centre, Royal Free Hospital, the programme currently operates in 42 cancer centres and hospices. She was subsequently elected Honorary Vice President, UK Cosmetic, Perfumery and Toiletry Foundation.

From 1993–5, she chaired the international working party on setting up Europa Donna, the European Breast Cancer Coalition and served as its first elected President (1995–9).

Founder member of the biennial European Breast Cancer Conference and member of its governing body (VZW) 1996–2005, Gloria Freilich co-chaired EBCC1 (Florence 1998) and EBCC2 (Brussels, 2000).

Elected FRSA in 2006.

Professor Kenneth Hobbs ChM, FRCS

Emeritus Professor of Surgery, Royal Free and University College School of Medicine, University of London. Previously: Consultant Hepatobiliary Surgeon Royal Free Hospital; Dean of Medicine, University of London; Chairman Systems Board Medical Research Council; Member Medical Committee University Funding Council and Higher Funding Council. Appointed member General Medical Council; Visiting Professor to Universities in the West Indies, Europe, the Middle East, Sri Lanka, Hong Kong and China; Honorary International Master Surgeon, International College of Surgeons; Honorary Fellow, The College of Surgeons of Sri Lanka; Honorary Fellow, Chinese University of Hong Kong.

*Professor Victor Hoffbrand BM, BCh, MA, FRCP(Ed), DM, FRCPath, DSc

Victor Hoffbrand is Emeritus Professor of Haematology at the Royal Free and University College Hospital Medical School, London. He was Head of the Department of Haematology at the Royal Free Hospital from 1973 to 1996. His early research at Hammersmith Hospital was in folic acid and the megaloblastic anaemias but subsequent published work has largely been in the fields of iron chelation and biochemical and molecular aspects of the malignant haematological disorders.

Victor Hoffbrand has authored and edited internationally used undergraduate and postgraduate text books and a *Clinical Atlas of Haematology*.

Dr Daniel Hochhauser MB, BS, FRCP, DPhil

Dr Hochhauser is a Consultant Oncologist at University College Hospital, London.

The Lady Jakobovits PhD (Hon)

Among her many community interests and charitable commitments in the UK and around the world, Lady Jakobovits continues to be an active and dedicated patron of Cancerkin which she has supported since 1987.

Philip Mishon OBE

The late Philip Mishon was a businessman who was involved with and supported many charities throughout his life. He served as the first Chairman of the Fundraising Committee of the Royal Free Hospital Breast Cancer Appeal, 1985–90 and as its Vice-President from 1990–2000. He then became a Trustee of Cancerkin from 2000 until his death in 2006.

Dr Lotte Newman CBE, FRCGP, FRCGP (NZ)

A past President of the Royal College of General Practitioners and a former fundraising gala chairman for Cancerkin.

*Mr Santilal Parbhoo MB, ChB, PhD, FRCS

Consultant Surgeon. Currently Lead Consultant Breast Surgeon at the Hospital of St John & St Elizabeth and Medical Director of Cancerkin. (See page 73 for biographical information.)

Miss Wendy Reid MB, BS, FRCS, FRCOG

Miss Reid is a Consultant Obstetrician and Gynaecologist, Royal Free Hospital, London; Postgraduate Dean, North Central and North-east London.

Professor Gerald Westbury OBE, FRCP, FRCS, Hon FRCS (Ed)

Formerly Professor of Surgery, Royal Marsden Hospital and Institute of Cancer Research; Dean, Institute of Cancer Research.

INDEX